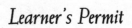

Learner's Permit

Learner's Permit

A NOVEL

by Laurence Lafore

Doubleday & Company, Inc.

1962

Garden City, New York

To George Brinton Cooper, Ph.D.

Dear George,

In youth, our careers composed an unusual geometric figure—they ran parallel and yet intersected at frequent intervals. You have known all the colleges that I have been connected with. The intersections have provided pleasant, if sometimes rather alarming, memories.

In the pages that follow, you may notice the presence of certain shades, of incidents not unconnected with yearbook editors, for instance, echoes from a past now very distant indeed. But you will also know, none better, that there never was such a place as Parthenon College, that the singular adventure of Nick Torrente never happened, and that the people in this book are none of them intended to resemble real people.

Yours,
L. L.

Contents

ЛПЛЛПЛЛПЛЛПЛЛПЛЛПЛЛПЛ

". . . . The being here represented is endowed with no principle of virtue, and would be incapable of comprehending such; but he would be true and honest by dint of his simplicity. We should expect from him no sacrifice or effort for an abstract cause; there is not an atom of the martyr's stuff in all that softened marble; but he has a capacity for strong and warm attachment, and might act devotedly through its impulse, and even die for it at need. It is possible, too, that the Faun might be educated through the medium of his emotions, so that the coarser animal portion of his nature might eventually be thrown into the background, though never utterly expelled."

NATHANIEL HAWTHORNE,
The Marble Faun

Part One

THE FIRST SEMESTER

Chapter I   *Matriculation*

A taxi drew up before the revolving doors of the Hotel Weigenhart in Acropolis, New York, and a young man descended, handed his bags to a bellboy, and entered the lobby to register.

He was a young man with broad shoulders, a determined jaw, and a dark complexion. His eyes and hair were black, his aspect emphatically Mediterranean, and both his coloring and the cast of his features powerfully suggested Sicilian forebears.

"My name," he said to the clerk, "is Hunter. You have a reservation for me."

The clerk consulted his records with a trace of hesitation. Then his manner changed. "*Doctor* Stuart Hunter? From Rome, Italy?"

"Right."

The young man signed the proffered card and turned to survey the lobby. Its wicker furniture, single potted palm, and worn linoleum were unpromising. There were not any spittoons, but their absence was noticeable. It was the sort of hotel lobby that seemed to call for spittoons.

The young man was eying it with a scepticism approaching disdain when his attention was diverted by the unusual appearance and behavior of its only other occupant, a gray-haired and rotund man, rather shabbily dressed, who had risen from a wicker chair and was approaching him with an odd sidling motion and an expression of bewilderment.

"Did I hear you say," the gray-haired man inquired, "that you were Dr. Stuart Hunter?"

"Right."

"An instructor of English?" It was clear that he considered the identification improbable, as if by some fantastic coincidence two Dr. Stuart Hunters were arriving in Acropolis on the same day. "You are the new *English* instructor at Parthenon College?" The profession of English seemed to strike him as even more unlikely than the name of Stuart Hunter.

"Right," the young man repeated, surveying him through slightly narrowed eyes.

"Indeed?" The elderly stranger looked at him thoughtfully and then, apparently deciding that he must accept the facts as presented to him, spoke in an entirely different voice. "Nutter!" he said with an enthusiasm just short of effusiveness.

"I beg your pardon?" The young man had a fleeting impression that the odd personage who confronted him was imitating a birdcall. But even as this impression formed itself in his mind he realized that it was not so much the result of any quality in the sound that the personage had uttered as of an association suggested by his appearance. He closely resembled a bird, an elderly, obese, and rather ruffled canary.

"Oh." He remembered now that Nutter was somebody's name and made efforts to place him. The Acting Chairman of the English Department at Parthenon, he thought. And no doubt a professor. He produced the title a little tentatively. "Professor Nutter. Glad to meet you." He added firmly, though as an afterthought, "Sir," and then smiled and put out his hand. Professor Nutter responded affably, but he withdew his hand hurriedly and looked at it as if it had been severely bruised. It was clear to the young man that hearty handshakes were not the custom in academic circles. He must remember to moderate his grip.

"I like to meet the new men when they arrive," Professor Nutter said. "I wanted to make sure you hadn't fallen into the ocean."

"Fallen in the ocean?"

"Airplanes," Professor Nutter said vaguely. "We'd rather have you here than in the ocean." He was still examining his hand, and he spoke as if the preference were a mild one. "We don't want any more sudden deaths. We need an instructor. A live one."

It seemed a reasonable need, but the young man received the words with an inward perception of irony. Although he fulfilled in the largest measure the requirement of being alive, he did not in any measure meet the rest of Professor Nutter's needs. He was not in any usual sense an instructor, although he hoped he was acting like one. The Acting Chairman's response to his handshake, like his initial show of incredulity, gave grounds for supposing that he was doing uninstructorlike things.

In this supposition he was mistaken. It was not his comportment, or even his handshake, but his appearance that had startled Professor Nutter, whose first reaction had been that Dr. Hunter looked less like an instructor of English than like a rising pugilist. A good-natured and rather good-looking pugilist, to be sure, but not one whose path through life had ever led him remotely near a college campus or among the enticements of the life of the mind. He looked much less likely to surrender to such enticements than to resist them. He looked, in fact, capable of resisting almost anything, including arrest.

He was certainly quite unlike any instructor in Professor Nutter's considerable experience of instructors, and in particular he was an instructor whom Professor Nutter could not conceive his late predecessor, Professor Clayfoot, having hired. Clayfoot's taste had run to the weedy, the languid, and the refined, and it was difficult to imagine anyone less weedy, languid, or refined than this.

Professor Nutter, however, was open-minded. The young man was presentable enough, and suitably dressed for his profession, if a trifle warmly for the beginning of September, in a tweed jacket and gray flannels. Professor Nutter had studied closely the dossier inherited from Professor Clayfoot in which Dr. Hunter's impeccable academic past was detailed; he knew that there could be no doubt about the orthodoxy of his intellectual achievements. And he was prepared to welcome warmly anyone who represented so marked a departure from the usual run of Professor Clayfoot's selections. He voiced some of these thoughts, cordially but with a persistent feeling that Dr. Hunter might swing on him if displeased.

"It is especially gratifying," he said, "to have a young man who has finished his degree. It is not satisfactory to have someone trying to teach and work on his dissertation at the same time. We have had some unfortunate experiences with young men in that position. Clayfoot was always hiring them. I welcome a Ph.D."

The young man nodded detachedly. He thought that Professor Nutter seemed harmless, although being unused to academic conversation he found his speech and the rest of his behavior eccentric. It was reassuring to be welcomed as a Ph.D. He was not in fact the holder of any degree, or even of a high-school diploma, but he felt no embarrassment in acquiescing in Professor Nutter's misapprehension. The latter appeared to perceive in his silent nod nothing beyond a becoming modesty, but his next words were startling.

"You are the marble faun," Professor Nutter remarked.

The young man jumped slightly. He was prepared to impersonate a doctor of philosophy but not a marble faun. For an instant he wondered how a marble faun was expected to behave; then he fortunately recalled that a novel of that name had been the topic of the thesis to which the real Stuart Hunter owed his doctoral dignity.

"Yes, *The Marble Faun.*"

"Ah!" Professor Nutter appeared to lose interest in Dr. Hunter's scholarly pursuits. "It's too bad about the hotel."

"How do you mean, too bad?"

"Depressing." He waved his hand about the lobby. "And dirty. But it's the only place, except for Ruby's Rooms."

"What are Ruby's Rooms?" the young man asked with lively interest.

Professor Nutter looked at him in surprise. "We don't recommend Ruby's Rooms. Not to our new instructors." He paused. "They water the drinks."

"Who does? Ruby?"

Once again Professor Nutter seemed unsettled. He was not, the young man began to think, accustomed to direct questions from instructors.

"The Weigenhart. The drinks are watered here."

"I see." Again he added after a moment's thought, "Sir."

"Well, I won't keep you now. You must be tired. Get along to your room. Ten o'clock."

"Ten o'clock?" The statement seemed not only irrelevant but inaccurate. It was six-thirty.

17

"Promptly."

"I see," the young man said falsely.

"Xenophon." Professor Nutter spoke as if he were explaining something.

"Yes, sir. That is . . ." One could not flatly ask one's boss—the young man supposed that an Acting Chairman was to be regarded in that light—what the hell he was talking about. "Ten o'clock tomorrow?"

"Of course." Professor Nutter looked at him benevolently but with mild reproof and repeated his previous instruction. "Xenophon. Xenophon thirty-six. We'll go into everything, and I'll take you to see the President. Have a good rest, Dr. Hunter." He held out his hand rather cautiously but added, "I shall call you by your first name. Goodbye, Stuart."

"Thank you, sir." The young man considered adding that he was always called Nick, which was true. It would save time and embarrassment and possibly risk—he was not certain that he would respond quickly if somebody said "Stuart" in a crowded room. It was barely possible that a person named Stuart Hunter might be called Nick by his intimates—a middle name, perhaps, or the corruption of some childish saying. But in considering the merits of this project he hesitated a moment too long. To suggest it after a protracted pause might set Professor Nutter's mind working along undesirable channels. Instead, he shook hands with a careful lack of pressure and proceeded to his room.

On the whole, he thought, things had gone remarkably easily, aside from the marble faun and Xenophon thirty-six. He felt both relief and satisfaction in his handling of Professor Nutter. But now he turned, in the reflexive manner of those newly arrived in hotel rooms, to the view from the window and suffered his first moment of real uncertainty about the wisdom of what he was proposing to do.

The greater part of Acropolis, New York, was spread before him. It lay on flat land in the river valley—whatever the associations in the minds of its founders, they were clearly not topographical—and the skyline was broken not by temples but by smokestacks. Acropolis was industrial, emphatically and obsolescently industrial. The mills were bleakly ruinous, and the wooden slums that stretched unpainted about them suggested that the population shared in the general decay.

In the center of this scabrous community, facing the Hotel Weigenhart on the opposite side of Agora Avenue, the main street, lay the campus of Parthenon College, enclosed in an iron fence surmounted by spikes of lethal and elaborate design, as if it were prepared for defense against the town in some primitive form of warfare involving an extensive employment of halberds. This hint of ferocity was fortified, quite literally, by the gateway that gave access to the academic stronghold, a considerable structure of red stone lavishly turreted and embrasured. But the college buildings, seen through the grimy verdure of the trees that fortunately cloaked them, suggested no justification for their warlike girdle. Built mainly of red brick, they appeared barely less utilitarian than the mills that besieged them. Aside from occasional concessions to the Middle Ages in the form of Gothic windows or flimsy donjons conically capped in slate, they looked like warehouses. The only considerable demonstration of an unworldly purpose was the college chapel, grandiosely proportioned and adorned with rose windows, which dominated the greenery.

The campus was unlit and appeared uninhabited. On the nearer side of Agora Avenue, by contrast, a profusion of neon signs and late shoppers presented a scene of restless

animation. On the roof of a large marble edifice a block
from the Weigenhart there flashed in red letters the alternate messages, "YOU CAN TRUST US" and "NEW
YORK US TRUST." At street level there was a positive
eruption of neon. *Eats. Drinks. Kampus Klothes.* Next to the
hotel, and almost immediately below Nick's window, stood
an emporium whose catholic wares were announced in the
largest sign of all. SODA, it said. *Biologicals.* NEWS.
Lunch. RUBBER GOODS. And at the bottom, in resplend-
ent pink letters larger than the others, *TRUSSES.*

He gazed at this panorama for some time with mounting
dislike and then retreated to the bed and lay down on it.
He was proposing, deliberately, to condemn himself to
residence for some indefinite period in Acropolis, New York,
and for a moment he wondered whether he could stand
it. He had lived luxuriously for three years in Rome, and beneath his outward air of resolute toughness he had been
permanently softened—or at least sensitized—by the artistic
indulgences of Italy.

The night before, he had sat for the last time on Lady
Tarragon's *terrazzo* and surveyed her justly famous view.
Her residence occupied a singularly favored site. Standing
several stories above its neighbors, its arcaded terrace rose
like an orange crag, vine-draped, above the Viale dei
Trinità. From that fortunate point of vantage the outlook extended in three gorgeous directions. Ahead stood
the regal pediments and towers of the Trinità dei Monte;
to the left, behind a screen of planes and pines on the em-
bankment, was a glimpse of the splendors of the Villa Med-
ici; and to the right stretched a still more magnificent prospect of rooftops descending to the Tiber and rising again
to the Janiculum, across which seemed to march a retreating procession of domes led by the distant majesty of Saint
Peter's.

These sights, as evocative as they were beautiful, exerted a powerful influence on all who sat on Lady Tarragon's *terrazzo*. Particularly at sunset, the potent distillment of their beauty was likely to induce a mindless trance in the beholder, an effect that Lady Tarragon had frequently relied upon in securing certain desired effects of her own. Nick was normally resistant to their magic by reason of both temperament and experience—he had been looking at sunsets from the *terrazzo* for three years—but he had last night observed the prospect with more than usual receptivity. The comparison with Acropolis was by consequence the more distressing.

It was on the same *terrazzo*, and at the same enticing hour of sunset, a month earlier, that the decision had been made that led to Nick's presence in Acropolis. Like all previous decisions in his life, it had been made, not cleanly or simply or on any reasonable basis, but simply as an impulsive reaction to a situation. He had been watching his employer, Lady Tarragon, devote her considerable talents to the beguilement of a young man who had recently appeared as an habitué of the terrace and whom Nick regarded with impartial disdain. His name was Stuart Hunter, and he had been in Rome for a year devoted to research on the topic *The Hawthorne Circle in Italy: Materials for a New Reading of "The Marble Faun."* Following an impulse to patronize the arts, Lady Tarragon had brought him under her patronage; now she was bringing him under a more extended form of it.

Dr. Hunter had nothing in common with Nick except nationality and age—they were both in their middle twenties. Dr. Hunter was a scholar of refined and languid appearance, and of strictly Anglo-Saxon ancestry. His good looks—he was undeniably good-looking—were of the pale and sensitive variety. His hair was blond and crew-cut, and his blue eyes, behind horn-rimmed spectacles, gleamed

with artistic eagerness. They also gleamed with an innocence that, in the Italian setting, was striking in any
male past the age of eleven. These qualities Lady Tarragon
appeared to find engrossing. And Dr. Hunter himself was
likewise engrossed, by everything that had happened to
him in the past year. He was visibly in love with Italy and
everything that it contained.

His temptress was of vastly more complicated aspect;
and the complications were entirely intentional. She was
a woman who much preferred to remain unclassified, and
everything about her—her age, her marital state, her nationality, and the sources of her present imposing opulence
—was clad in mystery. At the moment, reclining on a
chaise longue and draped in velvet, her features delicately
shadowed, she was exactly what she wished to be: mys-
teriously, agelessly lovely.

Dr. Hunter, diverting his gaze from the towers of the
Trinità dei Monte, now gloriously lit by sunset, sipped his
drink, stared at his hostess with decorous lust, and uttered
words poignant with intimations of unconditional surrender.

"'The day thou seest as mortality,'" he observed with
the complacency of someone confident that his quotation
will not be identified by his audience, "'But night is
dead at dawn and born in sunsets.'"

"Charming," Lady Tarragon said.

"William Cowper," Dr. Hunter explained.

"Ah." There was no doubt that she was impressed by
his poetic lore. "I am so glad you find the sunset inspiring."

"A birth symbol!"

"Ah." She sighed sympathetically. "And Rome? You find
Rome inspiring as well?"

Dr. Hunter paused, groping for another quotation.
"'Rome,'" he said at length, thrillingly but without this

ONE

time identifying his source, "'thy fascination sits upon me like a sorcerer's cap.'"

"Ah," Lady Tarragon said a third time, looking at him with an expression that in anyone less velvety might have been described as calculating.

Nick was accustomed to scenes of this sort. While engaged in patronizing the arts, Lady Tarragon was quite unable to resist beguiling the artist, and in his three years as her private secretary he had observed the process many times repeated. But the exchange just concluded, and the expression that could not be called calculating, convinced him that Dr. Hunter was destined to play a more substantial role in Lady Tarragon's life than previous beguilees. It was becoming clear to him, in fact, that Dr. Hunter was to be his successor. Even before Hunter's first appearance on the terrace he had been aware that his tenure was approaching its end. Three years was a long time for Lady Tarragon. She was a woman who liked change.

His conclusion was almost immediately confirmed, and for a time at least he was able to watch its confirmation with no emotion more profound than mild amusement. Toward Hunter, whom he regarded with a deep lack of interest, he felt nothing but detached contempt. Toward Lady Tarragon he felt no sense of outrage. He did not expect high standards of moral conduct in others, since his own moral sense was as near to being undeveloped as it is possible for anyone's to be. And he had no doubts of his ability to adapt satisfactorily to the position of Lady Tarragon's ex-private secretary. In the course of his progress from Chicago slums to the *terrazzo*, he had adapted satisfactorily to many more trying positions than that, and it was with good-natured tolerance that he observed the progress of his employer's suit.

"If you find Rome inspiring," she had remarked softly

23

in response to Dr. Hunter's second quotation, "surely we could arrange for you to stay longer?"

Dr. Hunter had demurred. His presence, he explained, was urgently necessary at Parthenon College, where he was to commence his teaching career the month following.

"But you could be so much happier—*here.*" She leaned toward him.

"Here?" It had come to Dr. Hunter that "here" did not mean merely Rome. His voice lost some of its metric dreaminess. "*Here?*"

His handsome, sensitive face vividly presented a mixture of emotions—joy, bewilderment, and embarrassment. So vividly that Nick laughed aloud. The participants in the dramatic dialogue thus brusquely interrupted had evidently forgotten his presence, and now, annoyed, they turned to him. His laugh, it occurred to him later, had been the beginning of everything; nonetheless, lying on his bed in the Hotel Weigenhart, he laughed again when he thought of the scene. And Dr. Hunter's subsequent efforts to man his shattered defenses seemed to him in retrospect no less comical.

Despite the power of his emotions, Dr. Hunter had sought with fair success to pull himself together and to answer with a moderately effective imitation of an urbane and condescending scholar. "I couldn't possibly, you know." He spoke with an effort that slightly diminished his air of casual patronage. "They need me rather badly there. I heard just the other day that they've lost Professor Clayfoot, the chairman of the department. A rather well-known Restoration man. It was he who interviewed me at Oregon last year—I've spoken of him to you. He died last week, so I could not possibly, in honor, let them down. . . ."

He broke off, and Lady Tarragon, shifting her attack,

had replied with an unexpected question delivered in tones unexpectedly brisk.

"How much were they going to pay you?"

"Forty-five hundred." Taken unawares, he answered automatically.

"I'll double it." Then she added in her silkier tone, "And of course, prices are much lower here." Mentioned by Lady Tarragon, the Roman price level sounded like some secret, perfumed vice.

"You'll double what, Lady Tarragon?"

"Diana," she said, whispering. "Your salary. As my private secretary. And as you'll live here, there'll be no rent. It will all work out—beautifully."

Dr. Hunter, visibly shaken, collected himself with an effort. "I know nothing," he said, "about being a private secretary."

"You will manage—beautifully. Nick can teach you all you need to know."

At this Nick had laughed again, and louder. There were implications in Lady Tarragon's assurances that struck him as both disagreeable and funny, and he looked at Dr. Hunter with an unflattering attitude of appraisal. "That's your business, Diana, not mine," he said. "You maybe will get tired of poetry."

"I am sure that I shall be quite satisfied," she said coldly, "with the way he will take your place."

"O.K.," Nick said. "So it's all set."

Dr. Hunter had been listening to this exchange with mounting annoyance. "No," he said. "My career. It would not . . ."

"Look," Nick said casually, "if I can teach you how to —balance Diana's checkbook, you can teach me how to be a college professor. In fact," he added thoughtfully, "I think it would be quite a lot easier."

He had intended merely to bait Lady Tarragon. But he

had underestimated her. She had raised one hand, as if in benediction upon them both, and had held the pose. Then she spoke, also in tones of benediction.

"What a splendid plan, Nick," she said. "Then Stuart would feel under no obligation to go back to America."

"Let us not be preposterous," Dr. Hunter said. "The man is illiterate."

"You don't think I'd be good at your job?"

"Illiterate," Dr. Hunter said again, with emphasis.

"Hell," Nick said, "I got all A's in tenth grade."

"An illiterate tramp." Dr. Hunter seemed fond of the adjective. "An illiterate . . ."

It was at this point that Nick had begun to lose his temper.

"Listen," he said, advancing.

"Look here," Hunter said, also advancing.

Lady Tarragon put a hand on both their arms. "No, dear Stuart," she said in wistful but compelling tones. "He'd beat you to a pulp in three minutes. He used to be a military policeman in Germany, you know, with the American Army. Besides, you don't understand him. He doesn't mean to be offensive."

"Offensive!" Dr. Hunter breathed deeply.

"He's just a little upset. Of course, Stuart, you're quite right in one way. He naturally doesn't have all your splendid education—how could he, considering his background? How could he be anything *but* an illiterate tramp?" And here she had paused, thoughtfully and fatefully. "On the other hand, he's very quick to learn."

At this moment the revolution in Dominic Torrente's personality had begun. Anger gave way to pride. Pride, inflamed, burned his heart. It had not occurred to him before to wonder what Lady Tarragon's opinion of him was. If asked, he would have said that he did not care. But to hear himself detachedly described after three years as an illiterate tramp ignited a blaze of something resembling moral indignation. His sense of proprieties as well as his self-respect—neither of them qualities of which he had previously been aware—were painfully affronted.

"This plan," Lady Tarragon was saying, unaware of these volcanic reactions, "has so much to recommend it. I should be quite willing to pay Nick a little pension so that he would suffer no financial loss."

"Ridiculous," Dr. Hunter said. "He couldn't last a week. Suppose they asked him about Spenser's influence on the lesser Cavalier poets? Or Frye's interpretation of Blake's view of Christianity? Or the conceptualistic ethos of the New Criticism?"

"Well," Lady Tarragon said, somewhat shaken.

"Or the crucifixion imagery in *Don Quixote?* Even on simple things like that he'd be shown up in an hour. And what about my future? My career?"

"You think I'd ruin your reputation?" Nick asked with real venom. "You think that at the professors' conventions they'd be telling stories about the Hunter kid who didn't know the crucifixion imagery in *Don Quixote* from his you know what?"

"Yes."

"Well, listen. Give me ten minutes with crucifixion imagery and I'll sound a hell of a lot better teaching about it than you, you damn . . ."

"It can all be managed quite neatly," Lady Tarragon said. "If for any reason things shouldn't work out, we shall simply explain to them that it was all a mistake and that your cable didn't reach them—it was stolen by a rascally fellow who, for sinister purposes of his own . . . And you have, after all, a whole month to teach him about crucifixion imagery and those sorts of things." She spoke as one disposing of a trivial inconvenience. "No one at this college, I take it, has ever seen you, Stuart, except this dead man?'"

Dr. Hunter, numb, nodded.

She turned to Nick. "All of Stuart's splendid qualifications, degrees and learned articles and so on, will awe them into silence. And it's such an opportunity for you. You always wanted to go to college. You told me so that first night that I met you, when we were walking in the Borghese, by the zoo. It is such a marvellous opportunity for—all of us. It will broaden Nick's horizons. They rather want broadening."

"He won't know what they're talking about," Dr. Hunter said. "He doesn't know the difference between *Ulysses* and *Moby Dick*."

"But he will learn. He has already learned so much in Rome—more than he imagines, I think. From my friends —painters, writers, people like Castani, or Gustav Spree. I regard the whole thing as settled."

Lady Tarragon folded her hands and stared at them benevolently. And they, in answer, were silent. The wildness of her imagination, the Gothic improbability of the fraud that she projected, had shocked them both. For if Hunter, a pure product of the graduate school of the University of Oregon, was chastely devoted to the principles of scholarship, Nick Torrente too possessed, as Lady Tarragon had observed, a reflexive respect for universities. But their shock was merely a preface to surrender. The chastity of Hunter's devotion was being radically reoriented; new stars had arisen to outshine the old. And for Nick the fascination of a university was supplementing anger, pride, and moral indignation.

The network of decision had descended. Uncertain of everything except his desire to beat Hunter at his own game, Nick had drawn the network about him.

"Listen," he said ferociously. "I'll bet you, Hunter. With

ONE

a little coaching from you, I'll bet you that I'll still have that job a year from now. I'll bet you a thousand." He had laughed, and added with a sudden resurgence of realism, "Dollars, not lire. Diana's dollars. O.K.?"

Hunter had merely looked back at the view, which had faded to a hazy diorama. His silence had been consent; and now Nick lay on a bed in a room in the Hotel Weigenhart and stared at the ceiling.

The ceiling presented another contrast, if anything more painful than the urban vistas. In Lady Tarragon's house his bedroom ceiling had been painted with frescoes of the late *seicento*, the work of an unknown master gifted at adapting scenes from the *Odyssey* to the cultivated taste of his day by the addition of large numbers of seraphim. The frescoes were charming and indeed noted. The ceiling of the Hotel Weigenhart was badly cracked. Its defects, inadequately concealed by dirty green paint, seemed so far-reaching as actually to threaten him with a rain of plaster.

Pained but resolute, he closed his eyes and prepared himself to face a new career.

Chapter II   Registration

*H*e dined that first night at the hotel restaurant, The
Porch of the Maidens ("The best in continental cuisine
served on a glamorous dinner terrace," it said on a card
beneath the glass top of the bureau). The atmosphere was
sooty, the outlook was upon an abandoned garage, and
the best in continental cuisine resembled fried gloves. And
Professor Nutter had been right about the drinks; two whis-
keys in the Cap and Gown Room had not contributed
materially to Nick's enjoyment of the dinner.

The Parthenon College catalogue, to which he felt
obliged to turn his attention, provided no after-dinner distraction. The text was not only unenlightening; he found
the obscurity of its allusions positively annoying. He was
beginning to feel that the vocabulary of education was
even more grotesque than the vocabulary of literary criticism in which Hunter had spent a month attempting to
instruct him.

Parthenon College [it began] was founded in 1847 under
the leadership of the Reverend William Wilberforce Barclay, Rector of the Episcopal Church of Saint John, in
Hudson Falls, New York, a distinguished classicist and
theologian who became its first president. Supported in its
early years mainly through the munificence of Adolphus
Kraut, of Troy, the college buildings were constructed and
the town of Acropolis laid out in 1850, and the college
opened its doors the following year to a class of six. Its
original purpose was to train young men of the western
Mohawk Valley for the Episcopal Ministry. Although it soon
developed into a liberal arts college with broad educational
aims, it has always remained true to the Christian Ideals of
its Founder, and students and faculty alike still receive
inspiration from its high traditions and from compulsory
weekly attendance at Chapel Services. While Parthenon
is today open to students of all faiths, Dr. Barclay's evangel-
ical ideals still shape its endeavor to inculcate qualities of
character and leadership that will fit its graduates for
adjustment to the society in which they live. First among
these qualities is a sound conceptual grasp of the Christian
ethos. . . .

Nick skipped to the next page of the catalogue, annoyed
by a sound conceptual grasp of the Christian ethos. At
some point Hunter had tiresomely explained what both
conceptual and ethos meant, but he had forgotten. The
list of Officers of the College that followed proved no more
lucid. Hunter, so far as Nick could remember, had never
mentioned the word "bursar," or any of the other cryptic
terms that appeared on page 2. His advice had been more
along lines literary and sartorial. Nick had been equipped
with the nearest thing that Rome could offer in the way of
suitable campus wear. He had also been equipped with a
short history of English literature and several lectures on
such topics as Water Imagery in *Henry IV, Part I*, the Incest Motif in *Hamlet*, the Class-Struggle Theme in *Emma*,

and Aristotelian influences on the poetry of Ezra Pound. He had been given an annotated list of people he ought to know about at the University of Oregon.

None of these were, for the moment anyway, more helpful than the catalogue's enthusiasm for the ideals of the Reverend William Wilberforce Barclay. The immediate problem was to converse intelligibly, assuming that it was possible to converse at all, with Professor Nutter, and with such other Officers of the College as he might encounter tomorrow. Doggedly he picked up the catalogue again and turned to the section listed in the index as Departmental Announcements. Under "English" there was a list of names ending with that of Dr. Stuart Hunter, Instructor, and then a long message which began,

> English A is required of all freshmen and is prerequisite to other courses offered by the Department. Sophomores electing the Classical Route are required to take Course 2–3, The Literature of the Ancient World, while those electing the Semantics Route must take Course 4–5. The Meaning of Meaning. Those in General Humanities are urged, but not required, to elect Course 6, Selected Masterpieces, not later than the second semester of their sophomore year.

Nick considered this passage and found it more preposterous even than the introduction. He was unable to guess at the meaning of its meaning. The Classical Route and the Semantics Route were totally mysterious, and the matter of electing them suggested a political rather than an educational process. General Humanities seemed not only mysterious but ungrammatical; surely it was in the nature of humanity to be collective, like sheep?

He skimmed the rest of the catalogue. None of it seemed much more informative than the Departmental Announcement, but one mystery was clarified. He came, in passing, upon several references to Xenophon Hall, and this edifice

33

he succeeded in locating on the Map of the Campus which
formed the end paper of the catalogue. But it was in a
state of irritation that he finally turned off the light. The
catalogue and its mysteries, coming after the best in continental cuisine, was not calculated to induce contented
sleep.

"Jesus Christ," he said to himself bleakly.

The room was illuminated in bold pink from the sign
outside, but presently he slept.

Promptly at ten the following morning he presented
himself at Xenophon 36 and was received by Professor
Nutter.

The Acting Chairman was installed in a large and clut-
tered office which, like the rest of Xenophon, wore the depressing dress of utility outdated. He sat at a roll-top desk
that appeared to be encrusted rather than merely piled
with papers. There were dusty books and filing cases on
every hand, a dilapidated leather chair, and a very large
photograph of Woodrow Wilson on the wall.

"The mattresses are lumpy," he said, evidently by way
of greeting.

"Yes, sir." Nick considered the mattresses. "But I was
tired."

He judged it proper to extend his hand and to clasp Professor Nutter's limply. For the first time he was experiencing some slight doubts as to the feasibility of his imposture. He supposed that in the next instants he would
be plied with conversation fatally concerned with Water
Images, Incest Motifs, and General Humanities. The process of ruin loomed briefly before him.

But ruin was postponed. Professor Nutter was inclined
to a garrulity so considerable that exposure would have
been impracticable, even on a voluntary basis.

"Well, my boy," he commenced affably, "we certainly

need your help this next semester now that Clayfoot is
gone. A great loss, Clayfoot. You know his work on Restoration Whores, of course. Always said to be the best thing in
the field, although I've never read it myself. I've settled
down with dear old Beaumont and Fletcher, on whom
there is still a great deal of work to be done, after a few
ventures on alien soil, such as my little study of the Vicomte
de Maudit and the poets of the Black Mass. You know that,
of course. But that was just a plaything. I'm back in London now. 1620, circa."

In the brief pause that followed this enigmatic statement
Nick judged that a knowing smile would be expedient, and
contrived one.

"The Department is very versatile. No one could deny
that. There's Oates, who is in the Middle Ages. Oates, like
myself, is a Full." Professor Nutter beamed. "There are
only two Fulls now. We *were* top-heavy, until poor old
Clayfoot went. Oates has just uncovered some work by a
fellow named Barber—or else he was a barber, it's not clear
which. Only a few lines, but it made quite a stir at the
meetings. You weren't there?"

"No, sir. I was in Rome."

"Ah, of course. He'll be bringing them out soon. Then
there's Pelz. Modern. And we'll have to get someone to re-
place Clayfoot in the eighteenth century. Too late to do
anything this year. Shalcross might help out with some of
the courses temporarily, but he's mostly in poetry. He's the
other instructor."

Nick nodded.

"I'm going to take you over to meet the President in a
few minutes. Ten-forty-five, Miss Scarlett said, but he's always late, so there's no hurry. I happen to know"—and
here Professor Nutter lowered his voice to an almost conspiratorial level—"that he's talking to Woodbine at the moment!" His tone indicated that this was a deed no prudent

man would mention above a whisper. "About the new curriculum. I suspect—in fact, I have grounds for knowing, although I won't mention what they are—that they are planning *further changes*."

Nick nodded.

"You know about the Semantics Route, of course. Well, now they're planning to make Semantics 1 a degree requirement. Even for science majors. What do you think of that?"

Since Nick had no idea 'what Professor Nutter was talking about, he had no strong views on the subject. Nor was he clear whether Professor Nutter thought that the proposed measure was to be welcomed or regarded with abhorrence, although obviously he felt strongly about it. There was a barely perceptible pause while Nick considered an appropriate response.

"Well!" he said at length, with heavy but noncommittal emphasis.

"I thought you'd agree with me," Professor Nutter said. "I'm surprised they'd dare try anything more, after the trouble with the new curriculum two years ago."

"The trouble?"

"Oh, yes. After Woodbine got the students to hang old MacIntyre in effigy. He never got over it, poor man. I always say that Woodbine murdered him. Wouldn't you agree?"

"Well!" Nick said again. It was evident that Professor Nutter was talking mainly to himself and that the need for response was minimal. He was restored to full confidence in his ability to handle Professor Nutter. He need not, he assured himself, have worried. The interview was peculiar, but it was manageable.

"Quite right, quite right. MacIntyre was an old crab, of course. But a sound classicist. None of this semantics claptrap."

ONE

"I see."

"I thought you would, my boy. But the President went right ahead listening to all of Woodbine's ideas. The President is crazy, of course, so we can hardly blame him." He paused and looked searchingly at Nick. "Gassed," he said unexpectedly. "He was a chaplain, you know, in the first war. Still a young man then, of course. It did something to his mind. He's been crazy every since."

This information Professor Nutter delivered in a brisk and casual tone, as if he were describing a blight affecting the shrubbery outside the window. "Nobody who wasn't crazy would have foisted the Semantics Route on us. Nobody who wasn't crazy would have hired Woodbine in the first place. Did Clayfoot tell you about the trumpets?"

"No, I don't think he did."

"That came before the Semantics. He put in trumpeting. For credit. For *credit*, mark you."

"Well!"

"I thought you'd think so, my boy." There was no doubt that Professor Nutter was pleased with him. "They played reveille and taps every day. Terrible noise. He had to give it up because there was some talk of disaccreditation."

"Of disaccreditation!" Nick achieved a tone that might be equally suggestive of horror or delight at this cryptic fate.

"Oh, yes. But that wasn't the last of it. The next thing he thought of was the Matriculation Rite. Nobody had ever heard of a Matriculation Rite before, but Overton visited some university in Germany and nothing would do except we must have Matriculation Rites." He cleared his throat with the faint suggestion of a giggle and then observed, "He's always liked the Germans."

"Well!"

"Colorful. Undeniably colorful. We march by juniority."

"Oh! By juniority."

37

"Yes. Juniority."

"Well!"

"I was sure you'd think so."

Nick had come to the conclusion that he was making a good impression. It was like making a good impression on a quagmire, for almost nothing that Professor Nutter was saying conveyed any substantial meaning to him. Still, he was doing well enough in dealing with these obscurities. Now, however, Professor Nutter showed signs of shifting from topics that had evidently been in the nature of a diverting prologue to more serious matters of business.

"About your load."

"Oh! My load."

"It is very heavy." Professor Nutter's birdlike head wagged sadly. "Everyone's is. Four units. I don't know how they expect us to do any work. I haven't done anything for years. Not since my Black Mass. That was in '47. Four units, and five in emergencies! It was Clayfoot's fault, of course, but nothing can be done about it at present. He let the physicists steal the march. Something to do with laboratories. I suppose Clayfoot told you about the schedule?"

"Only in general terms," Nick said cautiously.

Professor Nutter laughed with delight.

"You put your finger on it. I congratulate you."

Nick smiled modestly.

"'General' was the word for old Clayfoot's thinking. That was the trouble with the Restoration Whores, of course. All the reviews said so. A splendid fellow, mark you. But imprecise. Well." The professor laughed again, and returned to business. "Two sections of composition to begin with."

"Yes, sir. Two sections of composition." It sounded to Nick like something in a plastics factory.

"It won't be difficult, but there's not much *challenge*. You'll find the themes time-consuming. But somebody has to do it. It's a prerequisite. And the preparation is light. You simply follow the syllabus."

The last sentence implausibly suggested big-game hunting to Nick.

"A three-toed syllabus," he said unintentionally.

"I beg your pardon?"

"Excuse me, sir. A quotation. From Cowper," he added wildly, choosing at random a name remembered from Hunter's conversation.

"Cowper, eh?" Professor Nutter frowned. "You younger men are all inclined to be pedantic. Mustn't show off in front of the students, you know. Pedantry rubs them the wrong way."

"Yes, sir."

"You have a copy of the syllabus, I suppose. Or perhaps Clayfoot forgot to send you one. He never remembered anything. Well, we have some extras here." He rummaged in a drawer and at length produced a somewhat yellowed sheet. "These are from 1951, but we haven't made any major changes. In fact no changes at all. Clayfoot was lazy."

He handed Nick the sheet, staring at him with something less than his earlier approval.

"Cowper," he repeated darkly. "Not my field, you know."

Nick scowled. He was becoming again slightly unsure of himself, the more so since he was not clear where he had made his mistake.

"Then, besides the composition you'll have a survey section. Sophomores. It's a seedbed for majors, so we must treat them tenderly. But you'll have a syllabus for that, too. And then your own course. I suppose you've already worked that out."

"Yes, practically," he said competently. He remembered some sort of outline Hunter had given him. It seemed quite possible that it was an outline of his own course. "It needs some smoothing out."

"The course hasn't been given since young Beaton shot himself. A bloody business. Upset the public relations people a good deal. But then I always say it's their business to be upset. They don't do much for their money, and their salaries are twice as high as the faculty's. Since then we haven't had any American man. Not, frankly, that there's much demand. There are only four signed up, and one of them may be thrown out. The case is still in the senate, but I'm afraid he doesn't stand much chance. A major, too." He leaned forward and remarked with some solemnity, "Moral turpitude. Moral turpitude in the Zeta house. The Zetas are always worst."

Professor Nutter laughed, and winked. His good humor appeared to be restored after the unfortunate Cowper episode.

"Oh! The Zetas!"

"Yes. They're the worst. By the bye, what were you?"

Confronted with a direct question, and one entirely meaningless, Nick's nerve tottered. For an alarming moment he supposed that the imposture had been discovered; that Professor Nutter had hitherto been merely toying with him preparatory to this last, shattering question. So shaken was he that he was for an instant prepared to make a full confession.

"Actually I was an M.P."

Professor Nutter looked at him quizzically.

"Mew Pie?" he asked. "I never heard of it. I don't suppose you mean *new* pie? My brother was a new pie. We were all disappointed. He was a *very* strong delta delta legacy."

Too dazed for discourse, Nick shook his head.

"I suppose there is a whole set of different ones on the West Coast. As a matter of fact it's just as well for a

younger man not to have a local affiliation. Embarrassing
sometimes. The Houses are a little—well, the better students are barbs. Is that the case at Oregon?"

"Well, yes and no."

"We definitely don't want the younger men to be mixed
up with the Houses here. Especially not the Zetas." He
winked again, his beneficent attitude fully restored. "I suppose we'd better be getting over to Barrowes. I'll show you
to the President's office, but I won't actually take you in.
Miss Scarlett will introduce you. The President and I don't
speak. We haven't spoken since that quarrel we had when
Miss Pilkington was raped." He paused and looked owl-
ishly at Nick over his spectacles. Nick was shaken. Taken
in conjunction with the hanging in effigy of Mr. MacIntyre
and the suicide of Mr. Beaton, the rape destroyed the idea
of calm and erudition that he had vaguely expected from
institutions of higher learning. Such sensational transactions suggested the prospect of a future day when professors would refer casually to the Torrente Exposure.

"As I think I mentioned," Professor Nutter proceeded,
"the President is crazy. But you'll find him charming.
Everybody does. Charming! When he's not asleep."

It seemed a reasonable qualification, which might apply
to anybody.

"Gassed," Professor Nutter said, rising. "Gassed *and*
crazy. But charming."

It was a combination of qualities that provided Nick
with no very definite picture of the President.

They made their way along an asphalt walk between
sunburned stretches of turf to Barrowes Hall, a one-story
building with large expanses of frosted glass that looked
as if it might have been a primitive plant for the manufac-
ture of some small commodity like chewing gum.

"Used to be the library," Professor Nutter said. "Then
they built a new one, in '39." He spoke resentfully, using

the impersonal pronoun as if it referred to an elusive but
hostile natural force. "Barrowes was faculty offices after
that, but they squeezed us out. Gradually. One by one.
They have it all to themselves now. Bursars and provosts
and deans and directors of development. Positively can-
cerous."

They entered a door set in a flattened Gothic arch, the
sole and pallid gesture to non-industrial uses, and found
themselves in a skylighted rotunda. In its precise center
was a desk with a vase of roses on it, and at the desk was
seated a young woman.

"This," said Professor Nutter with a gesture of avian
courtliness somewhere between a bow and a sweep of the
hand, "is our new man. This is Miss Scarlett."

Miss Scarlett gave them a searching but friendly look.
She regarded Nick with what was evidently surprise, for
she paused, staring, before she spoke. "Dr. Hunter? The
President *is* expecting you, but he's not quite ready. I'm
afraid we're running a little behind. Dr. Woodbine is still
with him, but he shouldn't be long now."

"I'll leave him with you, then. And I'll see you tomorrow,
Stuart." Professor Nutter shook hands warmly and departed.

For a moment, Nick and Miss Scarlett were silent. She
was still looking at him, appraisingly and with something
approaching disbelief, a look not entirely different from
that with which he had first been greeted by Professor
Nutter the evening before. "So you are Dr. Hunter?" she
said.

"Yes, Ma'am."

His bravado was now fully restored, and he looked at
her carefully if somewhat condescendingly, since she was
the first woman he had seen that morning. About thirty, he
judged. So far as appearance went she belied her name,
for her coloration was neutral. Gray eyes. Indeterminately

brown hair. No lipstick. A gray-green suit which fitted too loosely. Regular features. He was not greatly stimulated; he was accustomed to respond to femininity only in much stronger doses than those administered by Miss Scarlett's clear eyes and clear, cool voice. But he was slightly stirred to perceive through a well-developed instinct in such matters that she was not only puzzled by his appearance but attracted as well. And he welcomed her straightforward look and manner as a symptom of sanity, the first he had encountered in Acropolis. So he added, casually, "I've just gotten in from Italy. I find everything rather confusing."

"I should think you would. You haven't taught before, have you?"

"That's right."

"After you've seen the President, I've made an appointment for you with Mr. Freeman, the Bursar. He'll take care of helping to find you a place to live. He's got one or two apartments you might be interested in. I assume that you'd like something furnished, near the campus, and not too expensive. That's what most of the new people want, and it's rather hard to find, but I succeeded in persuading Mr. Freeman to hold a few in reserve until you got here."

"That was very nice of you."

"Of course, chairmen of departments usually arrange these things. But your department was so much disturbed by Dr. Clayfoot's death, and I found out that Dr. Nutter had not—been able to see to it."

Nick's opinion of Miss Scarlett began to rise.

"You're from the University of Oregon, aren't you?" she proceeded. "I believe you know Dr. Campion there. He's a very old friend of my father's—my father is Dean Scarlett, you know, the Dean of Students here. I think that Dr. Campion wrote for you—I remember seeing the letter when I was getting the dossier together for the President."

Nick's opinion began to decline. She was venturing on

ground he preferred to have remain untrod, and she was showing herself capable of the syntax and vocabulary that he had found so distasteful in Professor Nutter's conversation.

"Yes, of course," he said. "A marvellous person, Dr. Campion."

He thought from her expression that he was expected to say something more about Dr. Campion. It seemed regrettably clear that the alternation of emphatic "Well"s with the last two words of each sentence would not prove adequate to conversing with Miss Scarlett. "He was very nice to me."

"And Clarissa?"

There was something about the way she said it that suggested a special importance attaching to Clarissa. He hesitated and then did the only possible thing. He repeated, as emphatically and as noncommittally as possible, the name. *"Clarissa!"* he said.

She looked at him penetratingly and hesitated in her turn. But she was sufficiently puzzled by his response to abandon Clarissa. "Dr. Campion seems to think very well of you," she said, "judging from his letter to the President. He wrote to Father, too, and he is anxious to meet you. You must come to dinner at our house soon."

"Very nice." Nick was a little breathless after this encounter. In Rome he had acquired the local habit of bowing formally in situations in which no other response seemed practicable, and now he did so, a little stiffly. She looked at him with renewed perplexity, generated perhaps by his odd formality.

This unexpected link with Hunter's past boded ill. Both Clarissa and Dr. Campion were threatening. He must consult Hunter's notes on personalities at Oregon before he met Dean Scarlett, but he thought it unlikely that they would prove sufficient to deal with any very searching inquiries. Still, he felt at the moment capable of handling even this situation.

Before Miss Scarlett could continue the conversation, a young man with red hair, black-rimmed spectacles, and an air of deep despondency so marked as to appear deliberately assumed came into the rotunda. Miss Scarlett rose to greet him.

"Ah, Mike."

The young man nodded morosely.

"Let me introduce you to a new colleague. Dr. Hunter, this is Dr. Kelly. Whom are you looking for, Mike?"

"Freeman," Dr. Kelly said. "Is he here?"

"Yes. There's somebody in there at the moment, though. Dr. Hunter is waiting, too, to see the President."

Dr. Kelly looked at Dr. Hunter for the first time, without much interest, but he held out his hand gloomily.

"Dr. Hunter," Miss Scarlett went on, "has come to join the English Department. He is in American literature."

"Is he?" Dr. Kelly said.

"You don't seem very cheerful, Mike."

"Cheerful? I'm submerged. Mentally, morally, and financially."

"I think I know what the trouble is, financially at least. But tell me anyway. Confide in Dr. Hunter and myself, until the Bursar is free."

Dr. Kelly looked up bleakly. "I might, if Dr. Hunter had a first name."

"Stuart." Nick spoke tentatively. It was the first time he had used the given name. For some reason it seemed to involve a degree of fraud more reprehensible than the last. "Stuart. Or Stu." The last was his own contribution. He doubted if anyone had ever called Dr. Hunter Stu. But it seemed more likely to encourage Dr. Kelly.

"Well, Stu, I'm Mike. This is Marian. You may not know it, but Marian is your best friend here."

Mike's manner was friendly. So friendly that Nick was conscious of a sense of shame. It was the first time he had experienced it since reaching Acropolis; quite possibly it was the first time he had experienced it in his life. The sensation was not agreeable.

"The fact is," Mike said, "there's been a mix-up in the pay checks. They've been undercharging me for the T.I.A.A. for a year. I got a letter from Freeman, who is sorry to inform me that there has been a slightly technical error and that I owe him a hundred and thirty-seven dollars and eighty-three cents, please. Well, I'm sorry to inform Freeman that I don't have a hundred and thirty-seven dollars and eighty-three cents. I don't even have eighty-three cents. I was waiting for this pay check to pay off a liquor bill of ninety-one dollars and seventeen cents, because the liquor dealer said that if he didn't get his money in two weeks he'd write to Purview"—he looked at Nick—"who, for your benefit, is chairman of the Department of Romance Languages and is in a position to 'terminate appointments,' as we say around here, and who is also a deep-dyed blue-ribbon, mineral-water-sipping bloody teetotaler."

"Jeez," Nick said. For the first time since his arrival somebody had troubled to explain something to him; and for the first time he was being presented with problems he could readily understand. He was moved.

"Look, Mike," he said. "I've got some dough. I stole it —saved it from the Fulbright. I might even have ninety-one dollars and seventeen cents."

Mike looked up, dejection replaced by amazement.

"That's awfully good of you, but—well, I couldn't."

Marian Scarlett was also looking at him, with appraisal as well as amazement. Nick realized that he had done, if not exactly the wrong thing, at least a peculiar thing.

"It's very generous," she said. "But fortunately not necessary. I've already seen Mr. Freeman, Mike. I think that everything is satisfactorily arranged."

"There's no possible arrangement that could be satisfactory."

"Well, viable anyhow. He was inclined to argue that it was your fault for not looking at your checks more carefully, and it seemed impolitic to point out that it was his fault for not making them out properly. So I told him all about your old grandmother in Ireland."

"But I don't have an old grandmother in Ireland."

"I know you don't. But you've been supporting her for years, since you earned your first pennies as a newsboy. Mr. Freeman's Aunt Bridget or somebody is Irish and he is devoted to her. He began to hum 'Rose of Tralee' before I was through. The debt will be amortized."

"What does that mean?"

"Well, in this case it means five dollars a month. Deducted from your pay check. It has an additional advantage to you. It gives Freeman a vested interest in having your appointment renewed, since the debt won't be paid off for years. And I think he'd rather not have the transaction made public. He's been rather sensitive about his bookkeeping ever since that affair of Dr. Winthrop and the stuffed crocodile in the Biology Museum. But that was before your time, of course."

In a moment of silence Mike Kelly looked at Marian Scarlett with adulation, Nick with astonishment. He was astounded to find that colleges not only contained a sprinkling of human beings—they were, in some cases, run along familiar human lines. The telephone on Marian's desk rang and she turned to answer it.

"God, what a woman," Mike said in a reverent undertone.

"I see what you mean," Nick said.

"Look here, I appreciate very much what you offered to

do. One sometimes forgets around here that strangers can be friendly; generally speaking the natives are not. How about coming to my place tonight for a drink? Thirty or forty drinks, in fact. Out of the ill-gotten booze supply."

"Thanks." Tentatively, he added, "Maybe you can give me some helpful hints on how to operate around here. It seems pretty different from Italy or Oregon."

Mike looked a little puzzled.

"Yes, I can see that it might. And maybe I can. Come around about eight. I'll get hold of a couple of the other people our age. I live on Stoa Street, on the other side of the campus. In a place called the Parthenon Arms. Number 217."

"The President will see you now, Dr. Hunter," Marian said, putting down the telephone.

She rose, and Nick followed her into an office on the opposite side of the rotunda.

"This is Dr. Stuart Hunter, President Overton," she said and withdrew.

The presidential office was large, stately, and ecclesiastical. The windows were traceried, the walls paneled in oak and decorated with portraits of eminent worthies of the past, two of whom wore miters. There were large, glass-fronted bookcases, and a chandelier with imitation candles. Behind an enormous desk, in a chair of almost episcopal outline and dimensions, sat the Reverend Helmsford Scantleberry Overton, D.D.

Nick's previous connections with religion were purely social, and despite the catalogue statement, he had only very foggy notions of the religious associations of Parthenon College. He had never to his knowledge encountered an Episcopal clergyman before, but he experienced a strong and instantaneous feeling that President Overton was a surprising, even an incongruous, representative of his order. He was an elderly but conspicuously robust man, and except for a clerical collar which peeped from above the top of a frayed turtleneck sweater, his appearance was in no way clerical or solemn. Besides the sweater, which was olive-drab in color, he was wearing corduroy trousers and carpet slippers. From his collar a freckled, rubicund face and sandy hair appeared like some unusual Australasian fauna emerging from its shell. His features were preternaturally large; they seemed to engulf the spaces in which features are usually set. Pale-blue eyes reached from nose to enormous ears; his nose stretched almost from hairline to chin; his mouth extended from jaw to jaw; and his chin protruded like an equine crag over his collar. Only one aspect of his visible person was not oversized; his neck seemed not to exist at all.

"Are you a boxer?" The presidential voice matched his dimensions. He spoke in a gusty bellow.

"No, sir," Nick said promptly. He was not entirely sure whether he was being asked to admit to being a pugilist or perhaps to some academic quality unknown to him. There was, however, something about Dr. Overton's manner that suggested the propriety of quick, decisive answers. He was prepared to provide them, but he found himself uncomfortably awed by the President.

"Pity. You have a boxer's build. I'm always hoping to find a sparring partner on the faculty. They run to tennis, though, if anything. A girl's game, tennis. What is your sport?"

"I used to bowl, before I went to Italy."

"Good. We'll arrange an evening at the Agora Lanes. I had two two-hundreds last week. Sit down. Now, tell me about yourself."

A strong counter-attack seemed indicated.

"What do you want to know, sir?"

"Well, let's start with your views on education. Are you in favor of audio-visual aids?"

Nick braced himself. Unlike Professor Nutter or Marian Scarlett or Mike Kelly, the President was uncomfortably inclined to direct questions. There were very few direct questions Nick would have welcomed from anybody at Parthenon, certainly not about his views on audio-visual aids. But the President's manner did not permit any hesitation. He took a deep, though he hoped invisible, breath.

"I'm for them."

"Good." President Overton struck the top of his desk with a clenched fist. "I like a categorical answer to a categorical statement. Scholars get into the habit of qualifying things. Do you know the difference between a college professor and a college president?"

"No." The brisk, resolute answer.

"A college professor is a man who every year learns more and more about less and less, and a college president is a man who every year learns less and less about more and more." The President laughed immoderately. "Now, tell me what place you see for audio-visual aids in the teaching of college English."

"A big place. But we need to know more about it. We need new approaches. We need more information. We need more experience. We need more—experimentation." Nick at last hesitated. It was clear that he was going to have to say something more substantial than this. But his remarks, if only prefatory, had clearly found favor. Indeed he himself felt a certain pride in this orotund beginning.

"Good. I agree with you one hundred per cent. Your entire profession, Hunter, is too old-fashioned by far. Nobody around here realizes the single outstanding problem of higher education today. *We must compete with television.*"

"We must *use* television," Nick cried with sudden inspiration. "We could have them look at—say, Shakespeare's plays. To give them a deeper understanding of the water imagery in *Henry IV, Part I.*"

"Umm," the President said softly. It was the first thing he had said softly since the beginning of the interview, and Nick construed it as indicative of doubt. But he could think of nothing to do but continue along the path he had commenced.

"Or the incest theme in *Hamlet.*" He was not at all sure about the propriety of incest themes, but they were all that came to him at the moment. "Or we could have dramatizations of Cowper. Or readings by poets, of their own poems. Poets like . . ." The names of all poets eluded him for a moment. "Edgar Allan Poe," he concluded weakly.

"Umm," the President said, more softly still. Nick looked at him in anxiety. His eyes were closed and his gigantic mouth open, his chin resting on his chest.

The President was sound asleep.

Nick was surprised but on the whole relieved. He felt that his peroration had been unworthy of his preface. And some of Professor Nutter's remarks about gassing were now explained. It seemed possible that his conversation with Professor Nutter would turn out to be like a movie seen backwards. In the fullness of time everything might be explained.

Nick wondered how long the nap was likely to last. It seemed best to go on talking. A sudden silence might awaken the President prematurely and cause embarrassment.

"There are," Nick said in a conversational tone, "a great many times and places when we could use television. For example . . ."

The President woke up.

"You're dead right, Hunter." His usual roar was resumed as if nothing had happened. "But I ought to warn you, you won't find that all of your colleagues agree with you. In

particular, you won't find that Nutter agrees with you. To
be perfectly frank, you're going to have to be very tactful
with Nutter. And with everybody else, of course. Particularly myself," he concluded unexpectedly.

"Yes, sir."

"I am the only person around here who is permitted to
be tactless. I have to be if we're to get anything done.
Things have to be done. The faculty don't see it that way,
of course. They complain because they're underpaid, but
they block anything that could get them more money. You
only get more money by experimenting these days. You
have to show the foundations you're out ahead in the race.
The professors don't like that. They say I'm debasing intellectual values whenever I mention television. They're
the most conservative people in the world, except in politics. In politics they're all radicals, and that frightens the
alumni.

"I could get them more money if they'd let me, but it's
like pulling teeth. You know about our Semantics Route,
of course. Well, that's our big claim to fame now. I'm on
the trail of half a million dollars to finance it because it's
something really interesting. Educationally interesting, I
mean. I got Woodbine in especially to run it. But it took
us three years to get it through as an alternative to the
Classical Route. Do you realize that this was practically
the last college in the country to give up Latin as a degree
requirement?"

"No, sir."

"Now, I'm the last man to criticize Latin. I once taught
it myself. But a college has to be first in the field, not last.

"I'm the oldest man around here, Hunter. There's an age
limit on professors, but not, thank the good Lord, on presi-
dents. But I'm the only one with any young ideas. Except
for Woodbine and a few of the instructors like yourself.
We'll have to work together on these things. I may say,

speaking as a priest as well as a president, that umm . . ."

President Overton's voice had trailed off into a murmur, and his chin fell once again upon his chest. Nick sat silent this time. Presently the voice began again and shortly recovered its full volume, much like a voice on the radio of a car emerging from a tunnel.

". . . the only hope lies with youth. You"—here he burst into a positive roar, and shook his fist—"are not fettered by chains of dust."

"No, sir."

The President looked at Nick with satisfaction.

"And now tell me, are you enthusiastic about the ceremonial aspects of education?"

"Yes, sir. Very."

"Good. I intend to work up—gradually, for the opposition is strong—to a procession a month. There is nothing like a procession to stir emotions, to evoke the ancient awe for the scholar, to stress to a materialistic age the link between learning and belief, between the soul and the mind. You can't have too many processions. I am sorry to say that Woodbine informs me that the soul has no reality, but even Woodbine has his crotchets. What we need now is a cavalry unit for the Matriculation Rite. There is nothing like a cavalry unit. But they're hard to find these days. The Fire Department isn't at all the same thing."

"Better than nothing, though."

"Better than nothing. This year we shall have the Fire Department, as a small beginning. But don't mention it to anyone. It is to come as a surprise. On November 11th, at our second procession. I am negotiating with the National Guard. How would you feel about wearing academic costume in the classroom?"

It was clear by now that the President always expected affirmative answers to his questions.

"I'd favor it strongly."

"Good. But that is a long time in the future. I shouldn't bring it up with Nutter if I were you. In fact I shouldn't bring anything up with Nutter if I didn't have to. Never volunteer, as we used to say in the Army. *Verbum sap?*"

"Yes, sir."

The President stood up. The interview, it appeared, was now at an end. Nick realized that the kernel of the President's message to him had been contained in his concluding paragraph, to which all the rest had been intended as an elaborate introduction. He was certainly prepared to follow this advice, having no inclination to volunteer anything to anybody.

"Thank you very much for your advice, sir. I appreciate it."

They shook hands, and Nick turned to the door. The business of leaving the President's office, which should have been the simplest part of the interview, was now seen to offer certain problems.

Two doors, identical and side by side, presented themselves to him. Both were closed. It was not possible to tell through which one he had entered. Nor was there any sign that the President proposed to assist him in a choice. But Nick had been in the Army, a fact that had been forcibly recalled to him during the past twenty minutes, and he was reflexively aware that in the presence of authority it is better to be decisive than right. Without hesitation he made his selection, opened it, and revealed a small closet containing a washbowl and toilet.

Unabashed, he closed the first door and opened the second. On the threshold the President stopped him with a rich chuckle.

"Just a moment, my boy." He turned. The President was smiling broadly. "I congratulate you."

"Thank you, sir."

"The choice of doors is a test imposed on all new men.

54

On some old ones, too, if they are foolish enough to forget.
You have passed the test."

Nick bowed.

"The lowest mark goes to those who ask me which door
is which. I have no patience with people who can't make
up their minds for themselves. The next-lowest marks go
to people who choose the wrong door and then apologize.
Or the ones who get embarrassed. The highest marks go
to people who do as you have done."

"Suppose they choose the right door?" Nick asked.

"I cross them off the list altogether. I don't like people
who deprive me of my pleasures."

The President laughed heartily. Nick bowed again and
left the room.

Chapter III   Orientation

At eight o'clock that night he rang the bell at Mike Kelly's apartment. The hours since his conference with the President had destroyed any elation he had carried away from that interview. He had been provided by Mr. Freeman with a choice of apartments, all of which struck him on inspection as sordid. He settled at last on one in a converted house on Theseion Street which had at least the merit of being old, so that its ceilings were high, its furniture agreeably oversized, and its trim of stained oak. And after an unrefreshing nap, he had dined again on The Porch of the Maidens.

The prospect of a life passed largely in the gloomy purlieus of Theseion Street, with expeditions to The Porch of the Maidens for diversion, oppressed him more than anything that had happened so far.

Mike's living room did little to raise his spirits. It was without a rug, and the floor and walls were badly stained.

There were an unmade studio couch and three armchairs in a regrettable state of disrepair and upholstered in some fabric whose precise color it was no longer possible to distinguish. There was a card table with a typewriter, a record player, and several very full ashtrays on it. And there was nothing else except a large number of books, most of them French paperbacks, distributed in piles on the floor. The scene was lit by one bare bulb, hanging by a cord from the ceiling.

The room contained three young men. Mike Kelly introduced the others.

"Stu Hunter. This is Sid Green. He's a chemist, so we don't discuss civilized subjects in front of him, to avoid embarrassing him."

Sid Green held out his hand. He was slender and dark.

"And this is Brandon Craig, who is an historian."

Brandon Craig was a muscular and sunburned young man with blue eyes and crew-cut blond hair. He looked more like something from the sports pages than an historian, but he rose from his chair awkwardly and walked forward with a deep limp to shake hands.

"Sit down," Mike said. "Or lie down on the bed if you like. In any case, have a drink. We've had one already—or to be accurate we've had quite a few—so drink yours fast." He disappeared into the kitchen and returned with a tumbler whose contents were a rich, dark brown, with one rapidly melting ice cube.

"And now, if Stu will excuse us, we'll just finish solving Brandon's little problem for him. You see, Stu, Brandon's been invited to read a paper. The deadline for submitting his title is day after tomorrow and so far he hasn't been able to think of anything he wants to write a paper about. So we're helping him. I've told him that if he gets a good title any fool can write a good paper to go with it. Then he can print it as an article and later expand it into a book.

Maybe three or four books. Now, listen to the titles we've thought up for him. He doesn't like any of them, but he's wrong."

"First," Sid Green said, "there's this, which I thought of. *God and Gold: The Colonial Policy of Ferdinand XII.*"

"Then," Mike said, "I gave him this, which is much better. *The Wages of Sin and the Price of Rum: Commercial Interests of the New Haven 'Saints,' 1724–1726.*"

"And then," Sid said, "I gave him the best of all. *Bride of Christ and Virgin Soil: Sister Polycarpa and the Conversion of the Illinois Country, 1690–1691.*"

"You see," Mike went on, "the rules are very strict. I've been doing research on it, reading old programs for historical meetings. The title has to consist of two short, racy co-ordinates which don't co-ordinate. One has to be religious and the other must deal with either money or sex. Then the subtitle must be long, expository, and boring."

"The only problem," Brandon Craig said, "is that there were no such people as Ferdinand XII or the New Haven 'Saints' or, so far as I know, Sister Polycarpa. I don't even think there was any conversion in the Illinois Country."

"Where are your powers of persuasion, man? Of course, if you like, you can change the details. There must have been somebody who had a colonial policy. And there must have been some place where somebody converted somebody else to something, sometime. We're just thinking off the top of our heads, man. Throwing our hats in the ring for the rest of you to shoot at, ideawise. If you listen to us, we'll be the making of you."

"It'll take more than you to be the making of me. However, give me a drink and try again."

"Isn't there anything you *want* to write a paper on?" Nick was genuinely curious.

"Frankly, no. I don't want to write a paper at all. But I'd like a slightly better salary."

"If you listen to us we'll get you one," Mike said. "How about this: *Martyrdom and Mastication: New Light on the Controversy Concerning the Fate of the Zenana Mission in Boola-Boolaland, May, 1878?*" He turned to Nick. "That will get him a higher salary if anything can, wouldn't you agree?"

Nick nodded. He had no clear idea of what they were talking about, but it seemed plain that the reading of a paper had some intimate connection with professional advancement in the academic world.

"It hasn't got money or sex," Mike went on, "but it's got chewing. People like cannibalism."

"Not historians. They're against it."

"Historians aren't people. Neither are teachers of literature, whether American or Romance. Some chemists are, although not most. Generally speaking, my friends, very few members of this faculty could be described as people under any strict definition of the word. Which brings us to the point. The purpose of this meeting is not to write Brandon's god-damned paper but to instruct Dr. Hunter in the peculiar *mores* of that singular *societas* known on the diplomas as *Collegium parthenonensi.*" Mike paused, projected his chin, and roared in a tolerable imitation of President Overton, "The regular meeting of this *societas* will now come to order."

"Speaking of *societates*, if that's the plural," Sid said, "do you suppose by any chance that Dr. Hunter is qualified for membership in the Club?" He was studying Nick with interest.

"Club?" Nick asked.

"Yes, an exclusive club, consistive so far of Sidney, Brandon, and myself. It's called the Specimen Society, and the membership regulations are very rigid. You have to be a specimen."

Mike too began to study Nick.

"He *looks* for some reason I can't quite work out as if he might be qualified. And although I haven't heard him talk much, he *sounds* as if he might be qualified. But I can't put my finger on the nature of his qualifications. Are you by any remote chance," he asked Nick, "a quadroon?"

"Or perhaps," Brandon suggested, "ever so slightly Communist?"

"I can't think offhand," Sid said thoughtfully, "of anything else that would qualify him. Unless perhaps you are a recently reformed alchoholic? But I'm not absolutely sure that would do."

"We better explain," Mike said. "It will tell you something about Parthenon. But first you'll need another drink, to prepare you."

Nick nodded. His glass was refilled. His interest was engaged. He was, in a peculiar way, enjoying himself.

"Now," Mike went on, "our club has another name, which is more descriptive. It's also called the Protective Order of Parthenon Instructors Who Were Hired in Order to Demonstrate the Famous Parthenon Broad-Mindedness. We are living evidence of freedom from prejudice. That is—or so we suppose—why we are here. I for example am an Irish Catholic, much out of place in this atmosphere, so I am evidence against charges of religious discrimination *and* snobbery."

"And I am a Jew," Sid said.

"And I am a cripple," Brandon said.

"You will observe," Mike continued in the best possible humor, "that they do not require very strong evidence of broad-mindedness. Moderation in all things. For although I am an Irish Catholic, I am not a very pure example of one. My father was once excommunicated. Also, I was born in Richmond, Virginia, which sounds genteel."

"And I am not very Jewish. My mother was a Congregationalist, and not only that but my father is an alumnus and generous benefactor of this institution."

"And I am not very badly crippled. Besides, it happened as a result of smashing up a training plane when I was in the Air Force, which somehow sounds more manly than polio in infancy."

"Now, Dr. Hunter, pray inform us what qualifications you may have for claiming membership in this select society."

Nick shrugged his shoulders pensively.

"Think, man. Is there nothing about you the administration would boast of—casually mention, say, over lunch in a New York restaurant, while negotiating with representatives of some liberal-minded foundation? Anything that would give conclusive evidence of their liberality? Or their constructive role in welding ever more tightly the bonds of American democracy?"

"Well, my grandfather was an Italian immigrant."

"Very good. Which one?"

"Both of them."

"Better and better. What were their occupations? Distinguished artists or opera singers, or even engineers, won't do."

"One was a barber. The other worked in a factory."

"Excellent. Here's to you." Mike drank. "They did well, no doubt. Sent their children through high school. Translated the family name from Cacciatore to Hunter. Put the favored grandson through college and graduate schools. It's a bit remote perhaps, but it will do nicely." He paused and frowned. "Did all this appear in the dossier? Did you mention grandfathers in your *curriculum vitae*? It's a little unusual to do so, I think."

Nick shook his head. He found himself suddenly uncomfortable. He had talked too much. He had no idea who Hunter's grandparents might have been, but they were almost certainly not barbers or factory workers or Italians. And he was becoming seriously puzzled about the motives of these affable young men. They were too affable to be entirely true; their conversation sounded too perfectly meshed, too much like a stage dialogue, as if they had rehearsed it. He began to search them for the intimations of a plot.

"If it wasn't in the dossier they couldn't have hired you specifically as a specimen. You don't qualify. Have a drink."

"I've still got some."

"Let me fill it up anyway. Sid? Brandon?" Mike took out four glasses and brought them back full.

"Now," Mike continued, "what's the next thing he ought to know about? Opportunities, I suppose. Are you eager to be informed about Opportunities, Stu, or do you prefer to make your own?"

For the first time that evening Nick understood clearly what they were talking about.

"I'd like information. It saves time," he said. The likelihood of a plot receded in his mind.

"Well, the answer, most regrettably, is none. Or almost none. Unless you have unusual appetites, and concerning such questions it would naturally be uncouth to make inquiries of a colleague. Assuming that your tastes run along usual lines, the opportunities in Acropolis, New York, are virtually nil."

"To begin," Sid said with the air of someone taking over the conduct of a committee meeting to read a report, "in the immediate neighborhood there are for all practical purposes only three categories of women. There are the ladies of the staff, secretaries, librarians, receptionists, and such. Most of them are (by design, we suppose) about ninety-six, and dead unattractive to boot—or to do anything else to. Three exceptions, if I have kept my books up to date. A girl in the Biology Museum, who dusts the exhibits. Un-

derage and not very welcoming. I expect she prefers TV
and pajama parties. In any case, there is a risk of statutory-
offense charges, so I shouldn't push it. Secondly, the Registrar's secretary. Welcoming. Definitely welcoming, according to reliable intelligence reports from the Zeta House.
But—according to those same reports—not wholly satisfactory. And the Zeta House ought to know. Third, there is
Marian Scarlett, a great woman."

"Yes, I met her."

"A very great woman. She's twenty-nine and looks thirty
but has the spirit of eternal youth. However, she's not the
type that appeals to all tastes and even if she were it is
known that she is unavailable. Research has been carried
out in this direction.

"Next, there are faculty daughters. Most of them are
mentally retarded—it's curious how many children of
learned fathers turn out to have minds of eight-year olds—
and the few who are not actually moronic and who are
within the specified age group have other handicaps. That
takes care of faculty daughters. Now we turn to faculty
wives. In general," Sid continued with a lowered voice
and a conspiratorial leer, "prudence and discretion pro-
scribe any fun and games with this class of women. Most
of them are unlikely to appeal. The few that do, it is unwise to toy with. There are exceptions to this rule—or rather
there is one exception—but . . ."

"Shut up," Mike Kelly said with sharp finality.

"O.K., O.K. No more about faculty wives. Now we move
outward among the teeming thousands of Acropolis. But
among those teeming thousands it is sad to report I have
not yet, after months of intensive investigation, succeeded
in uncovering much that is interesting to a sensitive scholar.
Prosperous Slovene assembly-line workers predominate.
They run to muscle, and early marriage. There is of course
the patrician element, but it resides as far out of town as

it can get, behind walls. Its daughters Come Out, but they come out only as far as the country club and we, my friend, are unlikely ever to see the inside of the country club. In fact, we are not likely ever to see a patrician unless a son gets thrown out of Harvard for procuration and repeated D's, and transfers to Parthenon. A number of them do. They staff the Zeta House. Parthenon is still vestigially fashionable as a third-choice alma mater for the hopelessly degraded and the inexorably stupid. It clings with withered tendrils to the Ivy League. But your contact with these scions of a noble tradition is likely to be limited to unpleasant interviews with their fathers after you've watched them move for a semester toward inevitable doom. The females of the family will not enter into the transaction.

"Thus, I am sorry to say, ends this brief review of available—or rather unavailable—opportunities for the bright young men of the Parthenon faculty. Have another drink."

"And now," Mike said, "we shall call upon Dr. Craig to explain the curriculum."

Nick took his refilled glass. He was impressed by the steadiness and rapidity with which his colleagues consumed blended whiskey. He was beginning to feel rather tight, but they gave no indication of any effects at all. Their fluency was certainly unimpaired.

"The curriculum," Brandon said, "is an object of considerable historical interest, displaying, like the government of Great Britain, curious accretions explicable only to the trained historian. Let us commence for purposes of simplicity with the Semantics Route. You know about the Semantics Route, of course?"

It was the third time that day that Nick had been asked the same question. He now was emboldened to answer it honestly.

"No, I don't. What the hell is it? What the hell is it a route to?"

"To the Bachelor of Arts degree. In our President's house are many routes to a degree. One may follow the Classical Route if one wishes. This means four years of either Latin or Greek. Or one may, as of three years ago, follow the Semantics Route. This means four years of Semantics, taught by a distinguished savant named Woodbine who ought, incidentally, to be shot. Things being as they are, all B.A. candidates, except three who stammer and are planning to become Anglican priests, elect the Semantics Route. This means they become versed in such useful fields of knowledge as The Meaning of Is, and Seven Forms of Ambiguity."

"It never occurs to anyone," Sid said, "that it might be more useful to teach them seven forms of clarity."

"Semantics is supposed to be an up-to-date substitute for a classical education. It was installed after a terrific battle, to provide employment for this needy Woodbine, who is a presidential favorite. Well, he got employment all right. He now has four assistants and is busily constructing an empire upon which the Acropolitan sun will never set. Very interesting example of accretion as an historical phenomenon. Next we turn to the entire question of the Core Curriculum."

"Speaking of cores, I need another drink," Sid said. "Stu?"

"No thanks. Not at the moment." Nick leaned back, settling himself for a long evening.

At various places and various times that day conversations were held of which Nick Torrente was the principal topic. The first of them took place during lunch hour in the Barrowes rotunda, between President Overton and Marian Scarlett.

Between them there was a degree of confidential understanding and mutual respect that would have surprised

the faculty, who tended to regard Marian as a friend and
supporter and the President as a subhuman and monstrous
foe.

"Well?" the President had said.

"I don't quite know." Marian was unaccustomedly tentative. "There is something unusual. Attractive, but unusual.
It may or may not go down well with the students—or with
everybody else, for that matter. I suppose we must rely on
his credentials." She considered for a moment, her eyebrows raised in perplexity. "I can't remember that I've ever
seen one before about whom I couldn't make up my mind
without resorting to the dossier. But in his case—well, I've
just gotten it out of the files to have another look. To see
him, it seems almost incredible that he passed his generals
with distinction and knows all about Hawthorne in Italy.
Since we *know* from the credentials that he did and does,
I'm rather optimistic. He's very good-looking and rather
offbeat and he's not likely to be dull. He also"—she paused
and tapped her pencil on the desk—"seems very nice. Kind-
hearted."

The President was also tentative.

"Good. I agree." This was not surprising; he invariably
did. "There is something very unexpected about him. He
doesn't, as you say, look like a man who knows about
Hawthorne. He looks more like"—the President pondered
a moment—"like the manager of an expensive but shady
night club. And his manner was odd. Generally, you know,
I'm bothered because they lack assurance. They pull down
their sleeves and uncross their legs and rub their back on
the chair. But this one had too much assurance. He was
polite enough, but I had the impression he was not greatly
awed by me."

Marian laughed. The President continued reflectively,
like some large ruminant chewing on its own thoughts.

"They almost always are, you know, whereas this one

said 'Yes, sir,' and 'No, sir,' and 'I do indeed, sir,' and all the while looked as if he were considering *my* qualifications. What surprises me most is that Clayfoot should have hired him. Clayfoot was a snob. He liked them more —gentlemanly. However," the President smiled, "he's sure to be an interesting change. Like you, I quite took to him. And there are certain reassuring features. I doubt if he's an alcoholic. I'm almost sure he's not psychotic. And I'm certain he's heterosexual. If we have trouble, I should anticipate something in the nature of a barroom brawl, or even a gambling ring. That would be an interesting change, too, on the whole."

Marian stood up and took her purse.

"My guess is that he'll be a success. Even a wild success. In which case you'll have trouble with Nutter and Oates."

The President nodded.

"That at least won't be a change."

At dinnertime, Eunice Nutter greeted her husband with impatient curiosity. She was a thin, grayed blonde who wore thick glasses and whose flaccid features concealed a sharp-pointed temperament.

"Well?" she asked.

"Well, what, Honeybunch?"

"What's he like?"

"Who?"

"Don't be a fool. Clayfoot's boy."

Professor Nutter sighed. He enjoyed his wife's brusqueries, although he would not have put it that way to himself, and he liked the interest she had shown in his professional activities since his elevation to the acting chairmanship.

"Fine chap," he said. "Sound on semantics. Sound on everything."

"I don't believe it. How could he be if Clayfoot hired him?"

For years Professor and Mrs. Nutter had subsisted on rudeness tempered by formal endearments and ancient jokes. Neither of them was aware of the impression this form of intercourse made on others. Indeed neither of them was aware that it had any characteristic form.

"Don't talk nonsense, Cherry Pie," Professor Nutter said. "Clayfoot wouldn't have hired him if he could have found anybody else for the money. It's a seller's market. Worse and worse for places with salaries like ours. Not Clayfoot's type, mark you. You'd like him, Honey. He's handsome."

For years it had been a playful pretense that Mrs. Nutter liked to flirt with handsome young instructors. It had occurred to neither of them that the pretense had grown grotesque.

"Light or dark?"

"Dark. Very dark. Mediterranean. Very sound on semantics, though. Well-mannered, too. Not like Pelz."

"I should hope not. But then you think anybody's well-mannered if they always agree with you."

"Bosh, Lovebird. But then if they agree with me it does show they're sensible, doesn't it?" Professor Nutter chuckled.

"Fool."

He chuckled again, contentedly.

Long after bedtime the Messrs. Craig, Green, and Kelly still occupied the unprepossessing living room. Nick had just left them, and as was their custom at such an hour they were all drunk and somnolently cheerful. Sid was slumped in one of the derelict armchairs. Brandon lay on the unmade bed, his bad leg stretched out stiffly before him and his good one, shoeless, drawn up. Mike was on the floor, his shoulders propped against a door-frame.

"Well?" Mike asked.

"He's rather an enigmatic Hawthorne expert, isn't he?

Monosyllabic." Sid sank lower in his chair; his voice was a little hazy. "Cautious, I'd say. Taciturn."

"He mightn't have been taciturn," Brandon said, "if we'd given him a chance. Looking back on it, I'd say I never heard such an unbroken flow of drivel from three normally sane men."

Mike laughed.

"There's something about neophytes that induces drivel. Tendency to show off."

"Tendency to give the wrong impression if one is too damned glib about the shortcomings of the beloved ivy-covered," Sid said reproachfully. "You ought to shut up about semantics and Woodbine and all that crap, Brandon. It's likely to get you into trouble as well as making the place sound more idiotic than it is."

"Speaking of shutting up, my dear Sid," Mike said, "you are likely to find yourself garrotted if you start burbling to strangers about Elsa."

"O.K., O.K., I'm sorry, Mike. But I didn't actually say anything."

"You would have if I hadn't stopped you. For God's sake keep your mouth closed."

"I will, I will. I may say, I rather liked our visitor. It's difficult to see what kind of teacher he'll be, but I rather liked him. It's just possible he might do something for that damned English Department. I don't see him swallowing Nutter whole."

"Or, for that matter, Woodbine," Brandon said. "He doesn't seem semantical."

"Semantical hell, he's barely articulate." Mike spoke with warmth. "But he seems sensible. And from what Pelz said about his work on Hawthorne he may even be a good scholar. Pelz read his dissertation—Clayfoot got him to. Pelz says it was routine, competent, and thorough. I must say, he doesn't seem to me routine, but it's nice to know

70

he's competent and thorough. Also, he may not talk much but at least he doesn't talk jargon. The word concept was never uttered."

Sid's voice had sunk into a dreamy drawl, barely intelligible, but he retained complete control over subordinate clauses. "In time, and by that I mean two weeks, I think we may count on seeing him aligned with us—that is, with the forces of intellectual righteousness. Beneath that dark exterior I feel sure there burns a true devotion to learning. If he survives, he'll be with us on the barricades."

"To the barricades," Brandon said sleepily, raising his glass.

While his late companions were discussing him, Nick in the Hotel Weigenhart was trying to get to sleep. He found it difficult.

Lady Tarragon would have been pleased by his present situation. In the past twenty-four hours, his horizons had been broadened to a really remarkable degree. They now included his first acquaintance with insomnia, with a sense of guilt, and with a failure of self-confidence. These additions to his education were deeply unsettling. Adding still another to them, he found himself staring at a ceiling phantasmically sprinkled with baroque seraphim and engaged in introspection.

"Jesus Christ," he said to himself, but his tone of voice was not the same as on the first night. It was, instead, meditative.

Chapter IV   *Intramural Sports*

Some ten days after Nick's arrival in Acropolis the President of Parthenon College and Mrs. Helmsford Scantleberry Overton were At Home.

The Home, like the President's office, was ecclesiastical in mood. Glum and Gothic, it ran to majestic dimensions, rubbed oak, lancets, and hangings of a dark Anglican green. On this occasion it was crowded with the Parthenon faculty which, reassembling after the distractions of the summer holiday, was being received. The annual event was designed to lessen the shock of going back to work.

Professor and Mrs. Nutter had escorted Nick to the festivities. They had seen him through the reception line, in which Professor Nutter had ingeniously and amiably contrived to avoid speaking to the President; he had greeted Mrs. Overton warmly and embarked upon a rather involved story about his marigolds which had carried him past her husband, to whom he nodded in transit. They had

73

then led Nick through a tangled mass of Ph.D.s to the tea table, outfitted him with a cup, and after exchanging further abstracted amenities and introducing him unproductively to a very deaf professor emeritus, had bestowed him upon Mrs. Overton. They had done, it was evident, all that could be expected to launch him. From now on it was up to Dr. Hunter to prove his social worth.

The President's wife encompassed the new member of the English Department with her presence. She was a small woman, but upon all who came within her social range she exerted a powerful effect; they were likely to have the sense of being crushed by graciousness. As she greeted him with expressions of ecstasy Nick drew back a step. She was blond, carefully coiffed, and trimmed with leopard skin. She was also handsome in a purely anatomical way, but she combined the more disquieting characteristics of the feline and the rodent. Her mien and regard were at once sleek and sharp. Her voice on the other hand had the quality of a double chocolate marshmallow sundae.

"You have only just come to Acropolis, Dr. Hunter? I don't suppose you have a large acquaintance among Acropolitans?" She laughed lushly, to indicate the insignificance of his lack.

"No, Ma'am."

"But perhaps you have met some of them elsewhere. Dear old Bishop Buddington, who is a member of a very old Washington family, has lived here since his retirement. Perhaps you know the family?" This was transparently a pretense. She spoke without conviction.

"No, Ma'am."

"You've come from Rome, I believe. What a *privilege* to have been in Rome."

"Yes, it was very interesting."

"I wonder if you knew of any of the people at the Embassy?" Mrs. Overton held a silken fan in her left hand—

74

the right being occupied with a teacup—and here she swished it languorously, emphasizing the significance of the question.

"Some." Nick was inclined to feel out the ground carefully. It was just possible that she might produce a Labor Attaché from the corner behind her.

"Did you, by *any* chance, know dear Hollingsworth?"

"Hollingsworth? No, I don't believe so."

"A dear friend of mine. Or perhaps I should confess—the son of a dear friend of mine. He is First Secretary, I think. Hollingsworth Morgan, from Philadelphia." She paused, and then continued as if her previous statement required elucidation. "The third. That is, not his father. Nor of course the old gentleman."

"Oh, *Bunk!*"

Mrs. Overton was unmoved. Her graciousness was proof against even a remark which appeared impertinent in both senses of the word.

"I beg your pardon, Dr. Hunter?"

"*Bunk*. Bunk Morgan, you mean. I knew him very well. We called him Bunk—" Nick checked himself. In the heat of the moment he had spoken without considering the pitfalls his avowal of Bunk Morgan might involve, but it was not this that had made him break off. He stopped out of delicacy. His next word was to have been "because," but it was better not to explain to Mrs. Overton why Hollingsworth Morgan III was known to his intimates as Bunk. It seemed in a way a pity; the anecdote might have pleased her, since it concerned a yacht.

"I see. How very amusing." She did not sound amused, but she was certainly interested. The President's wife was by profession first and foremost a hostess. She was secondly a snob, both by duty and by inclination. It was, she conceived, her role to present the college in the best possible light to the people who mattered—trustees, the rich and

75

the mighty—and for the most part new members of the faculty gave her little material to work with. For all his odd, abrupt manner, she found Dr. Hunter a pleasant surprise. In her previous experience, Fulbright students had been separated by a wide gap from Philadelphians named Hollingsworth Morgan. "Such a charming boy," she went on. "A connection of mine, although distant. You knew him well, you say?"

"Well, pretty well." Nick was not disposed to press the matter.

"I have another very dear friend in Rome. I don't suppose you would have run into her, though." Mrs. Overton's graciousness was now positively suffocating. "A very old and very dear friend, though I haven't been in touch with her recently. She was in school with me, so you can imagine how long I've known her." She bridled with an odd, squirming motion, and drew back her lips from her teeth.

Nick gave the requisite nugatory smile. She continued with triumph: "The Princess Marina di Massa! *Lucy* Marina di Massa, of course, not the dear old Principessa. Such a marvellous palazzo, off the Via Spumante. I used to stay there in our salad days. It was a great *privilege* for a young American girl. The tapestries! And the candlelight! A positive flood of candlelight." Warmed by these memories, she fanned herself furiously.

"I had dinner there last month. They still have the candles. There's no electric light."

"You *know* Lucy Marina di Massa?"

"Yes, very well," Nick said recklessly.

"And *dear* little Vittorio?"

"He's dead. The Resistance hung him upside down from a balcony in the Piazza Tortoni in 1944."

For an instant the finely mortised cabinetry of Mrs. Overton's graciousness showed signs of cracking. But only for an instant.

"I see. How very sad," she said with the effusive lack of interest with which well-bred persons respond to the small sorrows of life. While her lips formed this amenity, her mind was busier than ever. Dr. Hunter was really quite a surprise. She was adept at the self-imposed task of sizing up new faculty members, but Dr. Hunter added a new dimension to the familiar range of sizes. It was certainly unusual to have her instructors profess intimacy with First Secretaries and Roman princesses, and to profess it with a succinctness that verged on discourtesy. It was far more unusual to have her instructors describe with still greater succinctness the macabre fates of dear little Roman princes. But if his courtesy were open to question no one could possibly doubt hers. She continued with uninterrupted graciousness.

"And those charming tapestries in the gallery on the *piano nobile?* They are still there, at least?" Her tone suggested that their survival might be expected to furnish ample solace for the loss of little Vittorio.

"They're still there. But the Princess had to sell the Canalettos, I heard. To pay the fine."

"The *fine.*"

"Yes. They slapped a hell of a big fine on her when they put her in jail."

"In *jail.*" Her emphases were as meaningless as those of a weary tourist replying to the remarks of a guide who, pointing out the attractions of some antique monument, requires a profession of interest. But she set down her teacup and put one hand on the door jamb.

"They sent her up for twenty years. That was in '44, too. But the Demos let her out after two."

"The *Demos.*"

"The Christian Democrats. They let her out when they got to power. They like princesses. They gave her back the palazzo and the place at Urbino, but they kept the one in the south. She was lucky."

"*Lucky?*"

"Most of those people got shot. Or strung up like Vittorio. At least that's what I hear. I wasn't around."

"*Indeed.*"

"Anybody who'd kept Germans in their house. She had a whole slew of German officers. But what I heard was that since she'd been a lady-in-waiting to the queen or something, she had a lot of friends, so they got her out and got some of her houses back. And I guess our Embassy went to work, too, although she'd given up her citizenship. But she was still related to a lot of those characters in the Embassy."

"Dear Lucy," Mrs. Overton said enthusiastically. The news that Lucy had been a lady-in-waiting helped to overcome her distress at the other revelations.

"Yes," Nick said thoughtfully, "she's a nice woman. I'm glad they didn't shoot her." He paused, sizing up Mrs. Overton with quite as much experience as she had brought to bear on him. She was a type of woman not unfamiliar to him, and he apprehended through some primal organ of social awareness that it was a type that was not displeased to be shocked. "Her boy friend is a good friend of mine," he concluded affably.

"You are, I believe, interested in Hawthorne?" Mrs. Overton's transition was perfectly smooth.

He effected a no less rapid transition while sipping his tea.

"Yes, I am."

"My dear grandmother, who was a Bostonian, or more accurately a Cantabrigian, used to recall having tea with Mr. Hawthorne when she was a little girl. She looked back on it as one of the great *privileges* of her childhood."

"I guess it must have been."

ONE

"Yes, such a privilege. I believe he was a relation—" Mrs.
Overton interrupted herself. For the first time in her life
she experienced a certain hesitancy about claiming kinship
with the great. "And now I must go see to the tea table.
Poor Mrs. Goodge must be quite exhausted. Do let me
introduce you to the Purviews."

She clutched at the passing Purviews and introduced
him. Then she proceeded to the tea table and the relief
of poor Mrs. Goodge. One thing was perfectly clear to her
amid the shocks and confusions of the past ten minutes.
Whatever else one might say of Dr. Hunter, he knew the
right people in Rome. To this fact she clung, and in the
moment that it took her to reach the font of refreshment
she was able to formulate certain little sentences which
might later be casually dropped into conversations with
trustees, and with the rich and mighty. "Our new man in
literature, Dr. Hunter, such an *unusual* person. He is a
dear friend"—she hesitated, mentally experimenting with
embellishments—"a sort of protégé, I gather, of an old
school friend of mine, the Princess Marina di Massa. A
lady-in-waiting to the dear qu—" No. That was excessive.
"To the Queen of Italy." It was satisfactory. Dr. Hunter
would do.

Professor Purview was, in his turn, engaged in welcoming
Dr. Hunter.

"You are interested in Hawthorne," he said in tones not
of inquiry but, it seemed to Nick, of accusation. "Nutter
told me."

Nick bowed his head in acceptance of the charge. Dr.
Purview gave the appearance of a gentleman of great
antiquity, not so much by reason of age as from a certain
archaism of manner and frugality of person. He was tall,
thin, and somewhat bent, and he affected a haircut so
exceedingly Prussian as to seem totally bald. He wore
gold-rimmed spectacles, and his teeth fitted badly.

79

"When I was teaching at Bowdoin," he went on with the air of one who has no clear conversational aim in view but feels that the mere emission of words may suggest one, "I used to go to Boston occasionally."

Nick bowed his head again, acknowledging the fascination of these biographical data.

"On one of those occasions I arranged a stopover in Salem, Massachusetts. I found it a city without charm. No doubt it would be more interesting to you than to a student of Balzac. I was at that time completing my dissertation. It was regarded as a daring project." His teeth clicked convulsively. "Yes, on the whole I daresay you would find Salem more interesting than I did."

Nick indicated a courteous unwillingness to challenge this proposition. He saw indeed no reason why it might not be true, although he had only a faint recollection of having heard of Salem, Massachusetts.

"Elsa," Dr. Purview continued, "has never been to Salem."

"Oh." Nick considered adding that this was a pity, but in view of the low esteem in which Professor Purview held the place it seemed better not to.

"However, we have been to Concord, haven't we, my dear?"

"Yes, we have."

Nick turned to Mrs. Purview. She had spoken with a strong foreign accent which he took to be German; she had in fact said "Yiss vee hoff." Nor was this exoticism the only striking feature of Mrs. Purview. She was a great deal younger than her husband, some thirty years at a quick guess, and she was startlingly beautiful. She was a blonde, one of those blondes with streaky hair and a somewhat pallid complexion set off by dark, sad eyes and full, sulky lips. She spoke sulkily, too, as if much put upon by life. But her face and her figure, if a trifle overripe, were nothing less than glorious; her aura was that of a somewhat sickly and very sensual Venus. She seemed as flagrantly mismated with Mrs. Overton's drawing room as she was with Professor Purview.

"Concord is a spot we must all cherish," her husband continued, clicking. "And Lexington."

"Yes, indeed." Nick spoke heartily.

"I am a member of the Society of the Descendants of the Founders of Acropolis. A patriotic service organization," Professor Purview said impressively. "I am in fact a founding member and a past president. On occasion we organize visits to the Nation's Shrines. Valley Forge, Trenton, Saratoga. And last year Lexington and Concord, and of course Bunker Hill. Elsa enjoyed our outing, did you not, my dear?"

"Yiss. Ferry beautiful. Ferry inspiring." She paused, as if considering with languid sensuality the attractions of the Nation's Shrines. "Kloppstockl" she added unexpectedly.

"Kloppstock?" Dr. Purview sounded doubtful.

"A poem I used to recite venn I vass in school. I vass reminded of it in Concord. A poem by Kloppstock, a Cherman poet. It vass called *Hermann's Death* and in it de poet vrote of beauty schpots. You do not know diss poet?" She addressed Nick, who shook his head. "It is as vell," Mrs. Purview said passionately. "A beautiful poem, but he vass Cherman. All Chermans are murderers."

Nick was obliged to revise his idea that Mrs. Purview was German. Her sentiments impressed him as extravagant; it struck him that she was slightly sub-normal. But he detachedly calculated that in view of her appearance it would be asking too much of nature to demand lucidity or good sense.

"We must remember to be tolerant, my dear, no matter how much we have suffered."

To her husband's liberal plea, Elsa Purview responded

with a noise which sounded remarkably like spitting. Professor Purview clicked his teeth. An awkward situation had undoubtedly arisen, and Nick was running over the names of possible poets who might offer a diversion. For the moment he could think of none except Cowper, a poet whom he had learned to regard with distrust, and he welcomed the approach of another faculty member to their group. This was a man who, like Professor Purview, was tall and rather slight and, like him, appeared to be in indifferent health. But unlike Professor Purview he had finely formed features and a clear and perceptive eye.

"Ah, William." Professor Purview greeted the newcomer with evident relief. "You have met Dr. Hunter, I suppose."

"No. I have interrupted you with the express intention of doing so."

"Dr. Hunter, this is Dr. Scarlett, our Dean of Students. And now, I think perhaps Elsa and I shall refill our cups."

Nick examined Dean Scarlett with a mixture of interest and apprehension. He was curious to see what Marian's father might be like, but he was uneasy at meeting the associate of that hidden menace, Dr. Campion. His research among Hunter's mementos had not encouraged him about the prospects of coping successfully with a friend of Dr. Campion's.

The Dean resembled his daughter only in their common heritage of clear gray eyes. He was thinner and more ascetic, and his features were more prominent. But his voice had something of the quality of his daughter's, a coolness and precision and a fine timbre.

"I have heard about you, of course," Dean Scarlett said pleasantly, "from Arthur Campion and from my daughter. It is nice to meet you at last."

"Thank you, sir. I'm very glad to meet you."

"I want to get to know you. We—Marian and I—would be very glad if you would forgive a last-minute invitation

and come to dinner with us tonight. Very informally, of
course. I tried to telephone to you earlier, but it is impossible ever to find anyone on the campus."

"Thank you, sir. I'd like to come." The last part of this
was not entirely true, but it was clear that circumstances
demanded it, and there was no point in postponing the
inevitable investigation of his relations with Dr. Campion.

"Excellent. We shall look forward to it. At seven, then,
at our house. It's 91 Muse Street."

"Muse Street? I don't know my way in Acropolis yet."

"It's not difficult to find." A small change, a sort of
relaxation, came over Dean Scarlett, as if the transaction
of a tiresome affair of business had been satisfactorily
completed and he could now expand. "Muse Street runs
across the south end of the campus, paralleling Theseion
Street to the north. The name is rather interesting. I don't
suppose you have considered the origins of Muse Street?"

"No. I'd say offhand it must be part of the Greek atmosphere they go in for around here."

"That's what everyone supposes." The Dean spoke so-
berly, but his eyes showed a slight glint. It was clear that
he was embarked upon some form of banter, some mild,
erudite mischief, from which he derived considerable satisfaction. "But it isn't. In my youth it was called Propylaea
Street. Now you will probably already have noticed that
our classical place names cause some confusion for the
local populace. Agora Avenue is usually known as A Gory
Avenue. And if a visitor heard Theseion Street referred to,
he might well imagine that it was spelt The See-In Street.
But Propylaea was naturally the most difficult of all. As
classical education declined and the mills took over
Acropolis it came to be called something that sounded
like Purple Ear Street, and nobody could spell it.

"The municipal fathers took the matter under consideration, and during the first war it was at length decided to

rename it in honor of some gallant victim of the Kaiser. But unfortunately our losses in Acropolis were very small, two in fact, and even more unfortunately those two were named Srpski and Crznoka. So with considerable resource the municipal fathers agreed to rename the street after the engagement in which those noble American boys had sacrificed their lives for the fatherland of their forebears." The Dean hesitated and glanced uncertainly at Nick. Having evidently concluded that Stuart Hunter sounded safely autochthonous, he proceeded. "It was the Meuse Offensive, and the name was accordingly adopted and instantly mispronounced 'Muse.' And thirty years later another municipal father, who knew nothing of American military annals and less of French geography but who had some vague acquaintance with classical mythology, concluded that the spelling 'Meuse' on the street signs must be due to a ludicrous mistake on somebody's part and had them all changed to accord with the pronunciation. The final triumph of semi-literacy. A series of symbols of our age and nation." Despite the irony of his voice and the bleakness of his conclusion, Dean Scarlett appeared pleased with this episode from local history. At least he was smiling.

"It would have been better," Nick said thoughtfully, "if they'd changed the spelling to Purple Ear and left it at that."

"Much better. Honest folklore is certainly preferable to either bookishness or patriotic grandiloquence. But honesty is as conspicuously absent from our scene as learning. Except of course for people like ourselves in oases like Parthenon." He looked at Nick with the friendly understanding of a fellow-conspirator in a large plot against dishonesty and ignorance. Nick looked at the floor. "We shall see you at seven, at 91 Purple Ear Street. And now let me introduce you to some other of your colleagues. This sort of thing must be very trying for you young men, but I'm afraid everyone has to go through it."

The rest of the At Home was indeed trying, not only because Nick found it both confusing and dull to be handed from colleague to colleague, each of whom alluded with polite uninterest to the facts that he had recently arrived from Rome and was a student of Hawthorne, but more particularly because he was suffused with embarrassment at the magnitude of his own fraudulence. Dean Scarlett's attitude of a fellow-conspirator was, he realized now, being repeated with variations by the rest of the faculty. Beneath their gibberish they were innocently welcoming him into the plot against dishonesty and ignorance. Their credulousness induced in Nick an uncomfortable awareness of fraud transcending simple imposture.

It was therefore with relief that he welcomed the appearance of the Nutters after a considerable lapse of time and tea. They were evidently resolved to see that their young man (for this was how they referred to him) did not outstay his welcome.

"We're going now," Mrs. Nutter said. "You better go too." Unlike her husband she was incapable of obliquity.

"I was just getting ready to."

"How did you make out?" She led him toward the large ogival archway which separated the President's living room from the hall.

"I guess O.K. Nobody threw anything at me."

Professor Nutter chuckled at this colloquial informality. "He can take care of himself, Pussy."

"Mutt," said Mrs. Nutter fiercely. "I meant, did he meet enough people. It's important to meet as many people as possible right at the beginning. It would be easier if there were anything to drink, but Claudia Overton is too tight-fisted for that."

"I like tea myself." Her husband was inclined to contradict her merely out of habit. "And it's not her fault. There's the Bishop."

"*What* Bishop?" Mrs. Nutter conveyed the utmost scorn for bishops in general and in particular for whatever bishop her husband might choose to refer to.

They were standing now on the pavement before the President's house, under a very large yew tree. Beneath its funereal shadows Nick reflected upon the distressing regularity with which Parthenon couples seemed to quarrel publicly. First the untoward incident of Mrs. Purview and the German nation, and now the even more untoward incident of Mrs. Nutter and the Bishop. In his recent experience such bickering was unknown; in his earlier environment it had taken the more frank and acceptable form of his father's striking his mother across the mouth. It seemed discourteous, however, to draw attention to the existence of a quarrel by withdrawing from the Nutters' presence, since their attitude suggested (what was true) that it was merely the normal course of connubial chatter between them.

"Of this diocese, Honeybee. He wouldn't approve of liquor."

"Since when has the Episcopal Church objected to liquor, I'd like to know? Have you forgotten that Parsley?"

Professor Nutter turned his affable, avian face to Nick. "She means Pursley, of course."

"Pursley or Parsley, what does it matter? Anyway, I'll never forget that night he conducted the Compline Service when he was so drunk he could hardly stand up."

"But you weren't there, Ladybug. And there was no real evidence that he was drunk. It was just that he was wearing a full-dress suit."

"Of course he was drunk. Hattie Hammersmith was there and told me."

"She told everyone else, too," Professor Nutter observed.

"It made quite a scandal. But no proof. I admit that Pursley was rather unreliable." He turned again to Nick who was struck by this further evidence of the proliferation of scandal and recalled to uneasy thoughts of a future Torrente Exposure. "Of course, the President is *chief* Chaplain. But he doesn't take Compline normally. Unless someone has died. But that was years ago, Lambkin."

"It was just as scandalous no matter when it was."

"I must confess that Pursley was not a good appointment. The President's appointments never are, of course. Unwise."

"*You* say unwise. Any sensible person would say disgraceful. A drunk as assistant Chaplain! Do you drink, Dr. Hunter?" Mrs. Nutter spoke as a woman who had graciously recalled her obligations to include her guest in the conversation.

"Yes. Sometimes."

"Good. A teetotaler is as bad as a drunk. I'm a great believer in moderation. I saw you talking to the Purviews."

"Yes, I did, for a while."

She laughed harshly and, Nick thought, with something resembling ribald innuendo. "What did you think of Elsa Purview?"

Nick considered. "She seems very young."

"She is young." Mrs. Nutter was patently aggrieved by her youth. "Young enough to be his daughter."

"That's not surprising, Bunny. After all, she *is* his daughter."

Nick started. "I beg your pardon?"

"Or was. Before he married her." Professor Nutter laughed.

"Well!" In the face of this peculiar relationship Nick felt it best to revert to his reliable monosyllable.

"Exactly!"

"You're a fool, Fred."

"Am I, Lovey?"

"You don't make yourself clear."

Nick felt more drawn to Mrs. Nutter than he would have thought possible a moment before.

"Don't I, dearie? Well, my boy, the fact is that old Purview married his daughter-in-law. It's legal in New York . . . Lithuania! . . . Korea!" He was apparently compiling a random list of places where marriage with daughters-in-law was legal.

Nick looked for help to Mrs. Nutter, but she evidently believed that any ambiguities in her husband's earlier statement had been sufficiently clarified. He had begun to guess, however, that Professor Nutter's obscurity was intentional, a form of senescent humor, and that he expected to be queried about his meaning.

Dutifully, he queried. "It's legal to marry your daughter-in-law in Korea? And Lithuania?"

"No, no." Dr. Nutter appeared pleased. "Young Raymond was killed in Korea. On a hill."

"Hill 242," Mrs. Nutter explained. "Or perhaps 424."

"In any event, he had just married Elsa. She is a Lithuanian."

"A displaced person. Fred never tells things right."

"Don't I, Poodles? Well, a displaced Lithuanian. The Trans-Siberian Railroad, no doubt. No parents. At least Raymond's last letter said that they had been killed during the Nazi occupation. So of course old Purview felt an obligation. He was *in loco parentis*. Not, as it turned out, *parentis*. But decidedly *loco*." Professor Nutter laughed immoderately.

"Idiot."

"He was a widower and she was a widow. Very good-looking and dependent on him. Shocking, of course, but given Purview's personality not surprising. The President was strongly in favor."

"Goatish," Mrs. Nutter said. "Very goatish. Disgusting."

"He took the pledge when he was sixteen, too. And he tithes." Professor Nutter, oppressed by the ubiquity of sin, sighed deeply.

"But he has been repaid. Or so they say."

"Repaid?" Nick felt some uncertainty as between the moral and fiscal aspects of this transaction.

"There are rumors. Disgusting."

"But we must not spread them, Cherry Pie."

"Fool," Mrs. Nutter said. "He's bound to hear them. Everyone has."

"Well, the luck of the Irish."

"What he means is, there are rumors about her and the Kelly boy. Well, goodbye, Dr. Hunter." She extended her hand and looked at Nick cordially, even maternally. "I'm going to call your Stuart."

"Thank you, Mrs. Nutter. You've been very kind."

They shook hands and parted under the yew tree.

Chapter V   Scholarship and Research

*P*urple Ear Street contained a row of gaunt houses facing the campus. Apart from a filling station at one end and a delicatessen at the other it had survived the commercial thrust from Agora Avenue. At Number 91, the Dean admitted Nick through a front door whose plate-glass panel was surrounded with a border of stained glass.

"The house," Dean Scarlett said, "belonged to my father. He was professor of philosophy at Parthenon, and he bought it when it was built in the late nineties. I was born here. When I married, my wife moved in, so I have never lived anywhere else." He showed Nick into the parlor and added with gloomy pride, "It is a museum piece, though a remarkably ugly one. Nothing has been altered since 1910, when my mother died."

The parlor was a small room, hung with khaki-colored wallpaper and crowded with obese chairs and sofas upholstered in brown velour. There were a number of low-wattage lamps shaded in faded yellow silk with tassels. On a square oak table in the center stood another, with a shade shaped like an umbrella and made of sheets of milky polychrome glass, attached by a cord to a pendulous ceiling fixture overhead. The chimney piece was of golden oak, like the rest of the woodwork, with pilasters of an improved Ionic design flanking shiny tiles of venomous green. On the mantel stood a great many brass ornaments including a number of miniature Norman milk pails and something resembling a spoutless tea kettle with a perforated lid which was designed, though badly, as an incense burner.

It was a room that would have been familiar enough to millions of Americans of a certain generation and social class, but it was entirely strange to Nick. His eye traveled from the fringed plush hangings to a fraudulently bronze statue on the center table representing some Attic deity, and then to a large oil painting which protruded at a thirty-degree angle from the wall to afford onlookers a better view of its aesthetic delights. It depicted a complicated scene involving a shipwreck, a distant lady doing her laundry in the sea, a number of cattle, several epicene figures engaged in an intricate gavotte or caper, a one-eyed giant, and in the foreground a second lady apparently knitting. Nick correctly interpreted this as a compendium of scenes from the *Odyssey*. Comparing it to the *seicento* frescoes on his bedroom ceiling in Rome, which dealt with similar themes, he inadvertently said, "Wow!"

The Dean laughed.

"It's dreadful, isn't it? From both the artistic and scholarly standpoints. I think that it is intended to be symbolic. The prominence of Penelope and the obscurity of Nausicäa I take to represent the merits of marital fidelity."

Nick also laughed. It was a relief to know that its presence in the Dean's parlor was not the consequence of a mistaken aesthetic sense but rather of some cryptic irony. The Dean's next sentence further confirmed this.

"But we shouldn't laugh too much, should we? Homer lived some twenty-two hundred years before the man who painted that, and we are only seventy-five years after. We are as much the epigoni of Homer's race as he."

Wondering absently what epigoni might be, Nick felt obliged to attempt a counterfeit of the Dean's learned mockery.

"I like the chiaroscuro." Here, at least, he was on safe ground. "From the general layout of the ship, and that woman with the arrows on the right, I guess the painter was imitating Lorenzo Costa. The *Regno di Muse*, maybe?"

The Dean looked at him with satisfaction.

"Quite right. You didn't spend all your time in Italy on Hawthorne, I see."

"No," Nick said truthfully. "But I've only seen reproductions of the Costa. The original is in the Louvre."

"If you know Costa, you will understand why I cherish that painting—and the rest of the room. Marian is forever urging me to change it. She would like walls of dirty white, I daresay, and no furniture at all. Just a few cushions on the floor, and perhaps a bleached-birch coffee table. She claims to admire bareness, or what is, I believe, called the Japanese Look, no doubt erroneously. But I won't allow anything to be changed. The solid bad taste of one's parents is preferable to the sleazy bad taste of the present day. At least it gives one a sense of continuity—or, more precisely, survival. The only way any of us can be sure we are still alive is by contact with familiar objects that are palpably out of date."

As the Dean was speaking, Marian had come into the room. Nick looked at her with pleasure and surprise and so missed the concluding words of her father's paragraph. She seemed slightly but definitely changed from the

woman he had seen in the chilly expanses of the Rotunda.
Her presence was still competent and commanding. But
the competence and command were changed, as if the
acute awareness of her professional abilities and functions
—which was the most striking thing about her in the office
—had been exchanged for equally acute awareness of a
domestic or even a biological role. She was commanding
now as a woman.

It was partly a matter of clothes. The tailored suit of
the office had been exchanged for a soft white dress with a
belt that suggested, decorously but unmistakably, the shape
of her body above and below her waist. Around her shoulders there was a stole striped in silver, black, and scarlet,
a design suggestive, Nick thought, of Greece, a gift perhaps
from some friend who had visited Athens. If so, it was a
friend with a poor sense of what would harmonize with
her professional self or else one who knew her well enough
to realize that her professional self was only part of her.
The stole was a little unconventional; it struck a faint note
of something bold and bizarre. The Mediterranean colors
against the white dress, against the Dean's parlor, against
Acropolis, New York, carried with them some sort of defi-
ance of all those things. In the office her regular features
and her cool gray eyes had suggested some fine modern
sculpture worked in stainless steel. With the stole they
were lit with the suggestion of ardor, of fires to whose
existence she was deliberately providing a hint.

"Are you talking about interior decoration?" she asked.
"Father insists that I am designing to blast his heirlooms
and reduce the house to a rubble of contemporary trash,
but he's quite wrong. I gave up long ago. I must say that
I long for some straight lines and empty spaces. Something
thin. But it's his room. People have a right to their own
settings."

"A more modern parent would no doubt say that you

had just as much right to your setting as I do to mine. I confess that it's hard to combat the point on logical grounds, but since one of us must give way it seems to me greatly preferable that youth and folly should cede to age and wisdom. And speaking of parents, if you will offer Dr. Hunter some sherry I shall go speak to your mother." He turned to Nick. "My wife is something of an invalid and rarely comes downstairs, so there will be just the three of us at table. If you will excuse me I shall just go pay her a short visit. How does she seem today?" he asked Marian, pausing at the door on his way upstairs.

"As usual." Marian sighed. "She says she doesn't want any dinner, and that we're not to let her stand in the way of our having a good time." Her voice was perfectly even, but there was an edge to it. Nick recognized that Mrs. Scarlett was a difficult invalid, and Marian, as if reading his mind, turned to him. "I'm sorry, Stuart. I'm rather tired, and there's no point in denying that I find my mother rather trying. Like most people who are perpetually unwell, I suppose. Will you have sherry?"

"No, thank you." He was watching her with great interest, and spoke rather absently. "I don't like it."

"Neither do I. Father does. It's an academic drink, and I feel I should like it, but I don't. There's whiskey."

He nodded, and accepted a glass.

"How are you coming on?"

"O.K., I guess."

"You haven't moved into your new place?"

"No. Monday."

"I hope you'll find it satisfactory."

"It'll do."

"In any case, you'll be glad to get out of the Weigenhart, I imagine."

"Yes."

The conversation died of starvation. His replies, he realized, had given it little enough to feed on. His natural inclination to brevity, fortified by a long experience that had instructed him in its merits, was now further deepened by the interest that Marian excited in him. As he spoke the requisite minimum of syllables he was staring at her with an intensity that as nearly approached rudeness as his laconic answers. Suddenly he realized that an effort must be made.

"I've met some of my—colleagues." This technical term he produced with satisfaction, as a novice in an obscure tongue might take pride in his first use of the dative case. "I like Mike Kelly and his friends."

"So do I." Marian considered. "Mike is an unstable youth, and sometimes a foolish one. But he is likable, and he has a first-class mind. It's an agreeable surprise to find a first-class mind attached to folly. Or at least to his sort of folly."

Nick found this sentiment surprising. He could infer from Mrs. Nutter's remarks what she had in mind, and he was struck by her approval of Mike's reported indiscretions. "By folly you mean . . ."

"Not folly in any literal sense. But he is sometimes irresponsibly hedonistic." She spoke cordially, conveying again a tenuous irony as if she regarded conventional morality—and her professional concern with it—as faintly comical.

"Hedonistic?" He frowned.

"Thoughtlessly." Marian evidently supposed that he was questioning the applicability of her adjective, although in fact he was merely wondering what it meant. "Not viciously, certainly. In his personal affairs." She paused, and then added cautiously, "In financial matters, for example. But he has a good deal of charm, and he is brilliant."

"Who is?" Dr. Scarlett had returned to the room.

"Mike Kelly. We've been talking about him."

The Dean, having provided himself with sherry, settled into one of the elephantine chairs.

"You know Kelly, then?"

"I've met him, yes."

"He's one of our most promising scholars. I don't suppose you've seen his book. It's rather out of your line, but he's done something extremely good on the problem of the ocean in Corneille."

For a moment Nick imagined that the Dean had made a slip of the tongue. It was surely easier to conceive of a problem of Corneille in the ocean than of the ocean in Corneille. But the rudimentary liberal education with which Hunter had equipped him recurred to his mind just in time to permit without noticeable pause a comment he hoped was appropriate.

"Water imagery, eh?"

Marian laughed enigmatically, as if she had just scored a point over her father. He glanced at her and spoke rather hurriedly.

"Well, ocean imagery at least. He discussed the adaptation of the ocean themes in Aeschylus. It involved some new approaches to the classic theater in France, and it's an absolutely first-rate job. And Kelly's a good teacher as well."

"That's because he's irresponsibly hedonistic, not because he's intelligent about Corneille," Marian said. "I must go get something for us to eat. Will you excuse me?"

Left alone with Nick, Dean Scarlett sank lower in his chair and looked at him appraisingly.

"We need more good scholars. Good teachers are easy enough to come by, but there's no point in a good teacher who has nothing to teach about."

Nick nodded. He was surprised by the Dean's testimony to the attainments of Mike Kelly, a young man whom he had judged to be merely good-natured.

"We've been fortunate in our new men recently. There's Pelz, in your department, and a really excellent young chemist named Green. Enzymes, I believe," he added vaguely. "And a young fellow in history called Craig. They represent our vanguard in scholarship."

"I met Green and Craig, too."

"Do you know about Craig's work? He is a late-Renaissance man. English. He was in London the year before last and came up with some papers of a practically unknown philosopher named Flackey, who turns out to have influenced Coke—his tutor at one time. It's a fascinating research job. The Dean of the Faculty, Pirbright, gave me the manuscript to read, and it's one of the most closely reasoned pieces of writing I've seen for a long time. The article isn't out yet, but I understand it's already made something of a stir. Craig is being spoken of as one of the authorities, which is remarkable considering his age."

This time Nick was genuinely startled. It had been merely unexpected to learn that Mike Kelly was an erudite authority on classical ocean themes. It required a drastic reorganization of his whole view of Brandon Craig to accept him as an authority on anything. Nick had no idea who Coke was, but to have influenced him was evidently a matter of some moment and to have discovered the existence of such an influence was of greater moment still. It seemed entirely implausible that the discoverer should be the same amiable young man who had said that his only interest in his career was a slightly better salary. The Dean's next remark was even more startling.

"Craig is really a dedicated scholar."

"He seems pretty relaxed." Nick was thoughtful. "For a dedicated scholar, I mean."

"It's a common affectation. Or at least a common mannerism. Possibly a form of snobbery. I imagine that it is more common in the East than in your part of the country.

98

I've often noticed that the best of our Eastern young men feel it necessary to conceal the fact that they have serious interests. I don't approve of it as a suitable bearing for scholars, but it is greatly preferable to the literal-mindedness that my generation of scholars suffers from."

"There's sure nothing literal-minded about Craig." Nick spoke with conviction. His horizons had suddenly broadened again. He was familiar enough with some forms of subtlety, such as Lady Tarragon's, but those forms had generally had as their purpose either veiled pretension or veiled profit. This was the first time he had encountered a form of subtlety directed toward self-deprecation. He was obliged to compare himself to Brandon Craig, who had chosen to present himself as incapable of thinking of a topic for a learned paper, and Dean Scarlett's scorn for literal-mindedness became an unconscious reproach.

"One sometimes wonders," the Dean continued, having paused to sip his sherry, "what an outsider would think if he could listen to a conversation of this sort. I am thinking particularly of one of our trustees, an extremely successful businessman named Trexler, with whom I spent a tiresome morning at a joint committee meeting. I think that Mr. Trexler would certainly conclude that we are quite mad or, what is worse, self-deluded, in supposing that it signified whether Flackey influenced Coke or not. Let alone whether Corneille's use of the ocean was intended as a variation on a theme by Aeschylus. And no doubt he would regard a dislike of literal-mindedness as downright immoral, not to say un-American."

"You don't think—outsiders have any respect for learning?"

"I wonder. I daresay they may sometimes respect it, but they think at the same time that it's rather ludicrous. It's our own fault in part. Like Craig, we tend not to talk to them about the things we really care for—we only display secondary symptoms of what appears to them as a futile and rather morbid love of the useless. They never see that for us it's the fundament of the universe—religion, morality, diversion, as well as our careers. What sex was to D. H. Lawrence," the Dean added a little defiantly. "Or business is to Mr. Trexler."

"I know." Nick was exploring his own memories. One of them, seen now in a new light, recurred to him. "In Rome I got to know an old character called Traspogliani. He's a priest, and he's a prince too, and he's got plenty of dough. He's ninety-six. He's spent practically his whole life working out the floor plan of some palace in Alexandria which got burned down about 300 A.D. Nobody knows anything much about it, but he knows more than anybody else. He used to go there and study the writing on statues and things, and he collected a lot of books. More books about Alexandria than anybody ever collected before. He's going to leave them to the Vatican library. But what made me think of him was that he did all this because he liked it. He never wrote any books, and he never talked much about it to anybody else because there isn't anybody else who knows enough to be worth talking to. When he dies, everything he's found out is going to die."

"A pity," the Dean said.

"I don't know. You say that scholars do things because they like to. If it's moral to love learning, then that's all the old bishop needs to do to be moral, isn't it?" He was asking for information; this new light on morality surprised and interested him. But the Dean took his question to be rhetorical.

"But surely one has an obligation to other scholars. And to the world in general, to make the fruits of one's life-work known?"

"Oh, does one?"

"I think so. I should have thought it was one of the

givens." The Dean believed himself to be engaged in a speculative discussion of scholarly ethics, slight but engaging. Nick, however, found himself seriously involved in a novel problem.

"I guess Mr. Trexler would think so. There's no point in being in business unless you produce the goods. The old priest didn't think so, though."

"It's a point." The Dean spoke with gratification. "Undeniably a point. Perhaps the purity of our morals has been tarnished by an assimilation of the commercial ethic. But on the other hand, suppose that Newton had never published?"

Having rashly plunged in over his depth, Nick now found himself obliged to swim clumsily to shore.

"Of course, there is that."

"Or Freud."

Nick shook his head slowly, expressing honest perplexity, and at this difficult moment Marian returned to bid them to the table.

The menu was of Marian's choosing, it appeared. Aspics and green salad. The Dean, he judged, would have selected more substantial dishes, perhaps mutton soup or a saddle of something. But if the food was Marian's, the conversation continued to be her father's.

"Tell me," he said, leaning forward over an aspic, "did you have a chance to do much in the way of contemporary Italian writing?"

His choice of verb produced a passing confusion. For an instant it suggested to Nick that he was being asked whether he had written much in contemporary Italian, but he was growing adept at the simultaneous translation of academic language into English. He construed "do" as "read."

"Some," he said.

"Whom do you find most interesting? I don't read Italian

myself with any ease, but I've kept up somewhat with the things that have been translated."

"Well, I know Castani fairly well."

Once again a misunderstanding arose. As Nick had taken the Dean's "do" literally, the Dean now took Nick's "know" figuratively. He had meant to convey, what was literally true, that Castani was an habitué of Lady Tarragon's residence and a friend of his, not to indicate any extensive acquaintance with his writings.

"Ah, good. I thought that *The Aurelian Way* was extremely impressive. I don't really know enough about the literary background—or the political or philosophical background, for that matter—to grasp all the allusions, but I think he is a serious artist. I wish that I knew more of what he was getting at, though. The character of Alberto is, I take it, supposed to represent the tradition of Garibaldi and the anticlericalism of the *risorgimento*. But I didn't understand what ideas Marco represented. You can inform me, perhaps?"

Nick had not read *The Aurelian Way*, and he had heard the Dean's observations on it with mounting alarm. But the final question was quite fortuitously answerable. He had heard Castani talk about the philosophy of his characters at rather boring length.

"Castani *says* that Marco was supposed to represent Marxism. There was some friend of his—Castani's, I mean —named something like Formaggio, some crazy name—who was in exile with Castani. He got killed in Spain. Marco was supposed to be him." He was aware that this was not phrased with the felicitous involutions of academic style, but at least it was something that the Dean didn't know.

"Most interesting. Of course, Marco was killed too, so it all works out, although I hadn't supposed that the characters were literally biographical. One wonders a little about biographies in a work of philosophical symbolism."

"Yes, one does," Nick said rather desperately.

"Aesthetically, it poses a problem. But the novel is clearly a work of imagination taken as a whole, so I suppose it is not a very serious problem."

"No."

"Now, tell me, do people there take Moravia as seriously as he is taken in this country? I have always . . ."

The conversation continued.

Nick realized as it proceeded that Lady Tarragon's prognoses had been remarkably well-founded in one respect. The people whom he had met through her were turning out to be useful. His instinct of caution had receded, and he found himself, at the end of his meal, with his elbows on the table, talking much as he might have talked in a *trattoria* in Trastevere during one of Diana's more literary phases.

He was not merely parrying the threat of disclosure as he had done on every previous occasion since his arrival in Acropolis. He was better educated, at least in the spheres on which Dean Scarlett was questioning him, than he had realized. Lorenzo Costa, Castani, Moravia, the researches of Father Traspogliani, were subjects he did know something about. The discovery surprised him and enhanced his respect for his patroness. It also enhanced his self-respect, which stood in serious need of enhancement. And rather oddly it enhanced his respect for Dean Scarlett. There seemed to be areas of intelligent discourse that included people on both sides of the Atlantic; those people were in some sort educated, and he and the Dean and Diana were among them. With the startled complacency of one who learns he is conversing in prose, he ate his ice cream.

Engaged in these agreeable considerations, he failed to hear the Dean's last few sentences. But now a question was

addressed to him which, though asked in the most benign
of voices, undid his mounting sense of contentment.

"Tell me," the Dean asked, "how is Arthur Campion? It
has been several years since I have seen him."

Nick had dutifully done his homework among Hunter's
notes and had found that Dr. Campion's name appeared
in them in a form not only unhelpful but in the circumstances positively ominous.

"Arthur Campion," the note had said, "Director of
Graduate Studies. Good friend of mine. Helped get me the
job."

An exasperating note. If Campion had helped him get
the job, clearly Hunter knew that a connection with Acropolis existed and ought to be elucidated. Nick was inclined
to suspect Hunter of malice, which did not surprise him.

"I suppose," Nick said with as large an air of heartiness
as he could summon, "that he's written you. You've probably had more recent news of him than I have." This
seemed to commit him to nothing. On the other hand, it
offered purely temporary relief.

"No. Not for some months."

"Well, even then you're one up on me."

"But I understood from his last letter that he was following your work in Rome." The Dean spoke with unsus-
picious surprise. "He commented with particular favor on
the draft you had sent him. He said he was looking forward to seeing several more chapters, which you had
promised him for the spring. I formed the impression of a
most copious correspondence."

"Oh, my *work*." Nick prolonged the word, not through
any intention of emphasizing it but from indecision as to
what to say next. "I thought you meant personal stuff." It
was the best he could do at the moment, but he realized
that it wasn't very satisfactory and injudiciously elaborated
it. "He never writes about personal stuff."

"Personal—ah—stuff?" The Dean frowned, although whether in perplexity as to Nick's meaning or distress at his diction was not clear.

It was obviously necessary to explain the unfortunate word by some reference to Dr. Campion's private affairs. His family? He checked himself; it was perfectly possible Dr. Campion had no family. Offhand, it was difficult to think of anything personal that was also universal. "Health," he said a little thickly, "his own work. His hobbies!"

"Hobbies?"

This was very irritating. Everybody had hobbies. Except apparently Dr. Campion. Desperately Nick plowed on. "He's been very kind to me. I know that he helped me get the job here." He had now exhausted his supply of information on Dr. Campion. Hereafter disaster must ensue.

"He's always extremely good with graduate students, I know. But he must have regarded you as something special. Surely it's rather unusual for the Director of Graduate Studies to take such an interest?"

"Oh, yes. He certainly has been kind. *Exceptionally* kind. He's helped a lot with my work, too." Nick spoke with an affectation of shyness, hoping that he was giving an impression of fumbling modesty.

"He's helped you? Surely the subject must be rather unfamiliar to him. So far as I know he's never worked outside the field of ornithology. Hummingbirds, isn't it?"

"His help has been more along—technical lines. He is *exceptionally*"—he started to say "kind" again and decided hastily that it would sound not only unconvincing but inane—"widely read."

The Dean hitched his shoulders as if to indicate dissatisfaction with the course of the conversation. Then quite suddenly his expression changed to one of genial cunning.

"Clarissa!" he said in quite a different voice. "No doubt you came to know Clarissa well?"

"Father, really," Marian said with strong but unilluminating emphasis.

"Well, yes," Nick said.

The Dean smiled and folded his hands. "I have not seen her for several years, but I thought the last time I did that she was developing great charm. Intelligence, too. And really rather attractive in spite of . . ." He broke off, apparently in some private embarrassment.

"Not attractive, Father," Marian said. "Terribly nice, but not attractive." It was fortunate she had spoken. Nick had nothing at all to say.

"And I suppose that she is—ah—less so, now," Dean Scarlett said.

"Somewhat less, I think." What the hell, Nick said to himself, is the matter with this Clarissa?

"As you know, when she was younger it was really quite a serious matter. I am exceedingly glad to hear that . . ." The Dean's embarrassment, however obscure its cause, was marked.

"Oh, yes."

"I always hoped that as she grew older she would . . . well, to tell you the truth, I imagined when she was a child that it must be glandular. But when I visited them three years ago, I realized that I was wrong. She overate."

Immediately Nick grasped the whole situation. He was, after all, accustomed to innuendo. It had been the chief conversational tool of Lady Tarragon and many of her friends. Obviously the Dean had conceived an attachment between Clarissa and Stuart Hunter and had, Nick guessed, decided that Dr. Campion's remarkable kindness to him was to be explained by his gratitude for a chance of marrying off an unpromising daughter.

It was impossible to tell whether there was any truth in

these notions. He could easily believe Hunter capable of contemplating a marriage with the gluttonous Clarissa as a means of furthering his professional career and then of abandoning her for Diana. In fact the prospect of Clarissa might account for the readiness with which he yielded to Diana's temptations. But it was pure guesswork.

He spoke briskly. "Well, when I last saw her she was on a strict diet. I don't know whether she kept it up. Dr. Campion, as I said, doesn't write about personal things. And I haven't heard *anything at all* from Clarissa since I left Eugene."

A gratifying look of disappointment appeared on the Dean's face. Nick, however, felt compelled to proceed still further.

"But someone else I know there did happen to mention when he wrote me that she's been going out with a Baptist minister."

"Father." Marian now spoke. "You imagine the damnedest things."

She laughed, and so did Nick, out of sheer relief. They rose from the table.

"I'm sorry that I've been monopolizing Dr. Hunter, my dear," the Dean said, "but now I shall leave him to you again. If you take him to the other room I shall clear up."

The idea of a man who could discourse with equal fluency on the works of Castani, the ocean imagery in Corneille, and influences upon Coke, engaged in clearing up offered Nick proof even more striking than the décor of the house that he was indeed moving in alien circles. Such a thing would have been as unthinkable as it was unnecessary in the well-staffed houses he knew in Rome; in his own family, his father would never have considered doing the clearing up and his mother would never have suggested it.

As they settled themselves in the parlor Marian once again displayed her facility for reading his thoughts.

"Father likes to do what he can to help out about the house. He feels I'm overworked, which is kind of him although quite untrue. You mustn't mind him."

Nick construed her last sentence as having an application wider than the Dean's wish to help around the house. It referred, he supposed, to Clarissa. He nodded.

"He likes to look for the inward meaning of things," Marian went on. "It sometimes leads to ingenious theories which are not only wrong but tactless. It's the academic mind, I suppose. If you are trained to explore all avenues, you are naturally going to be led down some rather peculiar ones."

"It's everybody, isn't it, not just the academic people? They are maybe going to find more avenues than anybody else, but most people are willing to explore any interesting avenues they notice. Too damned willing."

"I suppose so." She looked at him, smiling, as if some esoteric understanding had been established between them by his entirely banal observation. There was an odd sense of unreality about the conversation, he thought, as if they were talking simply to conceal their thoughts. "But don't you think that the trained mind is particularly difficult to deal with socially? I don't suppose you do, though. Having one yourself you can't judge what it's like to watch one in action."

He considered his answer carefully, seeking a compromise between candor and caution.

"It's possible. But my mind isn't as trained as you might think. Not yet, anyway. I've had more to do with people who weren't college professors than with ones who were."

"Yes, I can see that you have. It surprises me. Judging from the *curriculum vitae*, I'd have thought your life had been almost as thoroughly academic as mine. I gathered you were raised in an absolute orgy of culture. It sounded that way. I have to read all the *curricula vitae*. I know how old everyone is and who their fathers were."

"It's a wise *curriculum vitae* that knows its own father."

She looked at him with one eyebrow raised.

"What do you mean?"

"Just that you can't tell everything from a *curriculum vitae*," he said with complete accuracy.

"No, I suppose not. Do you mean that you were really raised in an orphanage and spent your adolescence in a reform school? It's perfectly possible, of course. We don't do any checking up on the years before the candidates reached college." The idea seemed on the whole to please her.

"In Italy I knew a lot of people who weren't exactly academic."

"It's a fair substitute for the orphanage and the reform school. To be quite frank, I find you rather surprisingly free from—the stamp, I suppose it is, of the cloister. I don't hold it against you, you realize?"

"No. I figured it that way."

"I get a little tired occasionally of the cloistral stamp. A change is refreshing."

She spoke with her usual cool detachment, but he perceived a wistfulness, almost a loneliness, in her voice.

Nick, whose greatest expertness and experience lay along precisely these lines, was by now aware that her interest in him was more than mere curiosity about a sport of the academic breed. His highly trained sensitivities had been informing him of this fact with mounting urgency since the beginning of the evening. But they were also informing him that she intended to do no more than play with her emotions. He was sorry for it, for both their sakes.

There was also, he realized, something more complicated in the barriers she was building around herself than the decorous modesty of middle-class maidenhood—something unexpectedly worldly and subtle in her motives.

In the moment's silence after her last sentence his thoughts were led from Marian to himself, and here too he found unfamiliar complexities. He was unused to analyzing his own reactions to women; in his past career he had found it sufficient to decide at first glance whether or not he wanted to sleep with them. But Marian's attractions, while powerful enough, invited no such simple decision.

"I can see that life here wouldn't be too—varied." He was surprised to hear in his own voice a degree of casual detachment that very nearly equalled hers.

"It's not a question of variety. To be quite frank there is something I don't *like* about the academic personality."

"Oh?"

She apparently misunderstood his surprise, taking it as a reproach for impertinence. "I don't mean it the way it sounds. I don't disapprove of it. I love my father, who is the most academic personality that I've ever known or can imagine, very much, and I admire many—I think most— of the people at Parthenon. They are quite the *best* people in the world. And I not only love my father; I respect him and the things he believes in. There really is a kind of morality in scholars that other people don't have."

"But . . . ?"

"When I say I don't like it, I mean I don't like it for myself. I'm not a scholar. I am an outsider who has always lived on the inside of someone else's world. I suppose it happens often—a child of musicians, say, who is tone-deaf. He may love music and admire it, but he is always an outsider. But the academic world is particularly tightly closed."

There was no complaint in her voice and certainly no self-pity, but he found himself touched by what, rationally considered, seemed an absurd dilemma. If she disliked her environment why didn't she leave it? But as the question occurred to him, so did the answer. She was obviously imprisoned by her parents' dependence.

"What do you think your proper world is?"

"I don't know."

"What would you like to do?"

"That's just it. There's nothing else I'd like to do, because I've done nothing else. I never could. By the time I was grown up it was clear that I was needed at home. You see, I've no identity of my own. Or rather, the only identity I have comes from resisting being drowned in a world that I love but am not part of."

"I know. Parthenon—any college campus, I suppose—is pretty—enveloping. You can get wrapped up in it awfully easy, I can see."

"It's very odd. You *say* you know, Stuart, and I have the feeling that you do. But I'm certain that you can't *really* know what I'm talking about. If you could, you would never have gone to graduate school and you would never have written a thesis about Hawthorne in Italy, and you would never have come to Parthenon to teach. So I can't believe you, because I know what kind of person you must be, and that kind of person can't know what I'm talking about. If you were a janitor instead of a literary scholar, and if you'd really spent your youth in an orphanage and a reform school, you could. I find it"—she hesitated a moment—"I find it hard to believe that you're an insider, but you are, and that's an end to it."

"Oh, hell."

"By which you mean . . . ?"

"People aren't that way, Marian. Everybody's got a lot of different selves, even college professors. People aren't *made* by their profession."

She raised her eyebrows again.

"You know, Stuart, no one could say that except some-

111

one who knew nothing about college professors. Unless he were one himself."

"Well"—Nick, abandoning a proposition that he regarded as both annoying and unreal, returned to an earlier and more manageable topic—"don't you have any idea at all of where you could go to—have your own identity?"

Marian considered. "No. But I think it would become me better to do something adventurous—not to establish my identity but to find out if I have one. Not the usual sort of adventure, not running off with the milkman or taking up narcotics. What would be useful—I don't say I'd like it, mind you—would be to face some shocking choice, such as whether to murder someone to save my father from disgrace and ruin. Unhappily nobody's ever going to be in a position to threaten him with disgrace and ruin so this is not very realistic. But some situation in which none of the rules I know would help me."

"In Rome you keep meeting people who are going somewhere to teach the natives of someplace to get rid of bedbugs. Is that the sort of thing?"

"No. I don't care whether the natives have bedbugs or not. I'd be interested in seeing whether I could get rid of them for myself. There aren't any bedbugs on college campuses," she said wistfully. "It would have to be some situation or some place where everything was all wrong. A school for delinquents, or a depraved aristocracy. Portugal might do, I think. I'm told that there is a really deplorable amount of debauchery among the Portuguese nobility. I think debauchery would be the best solution."

"I don't really see you being debauched."

"I don't think I'd want to become debauched personally. At least not at first. But that's really the point. I'd like to know how I felt about debauchery after I'd seen some of it. To see whether I could handle a world where everything was wrong. Of course it might turn out that I would take to it very well, but I see my role in the Portuguese nobility more as that of the person who doesn't take to it. Perhaps as the understanding and helpful wife of a really debased marquis."

"It could be that you'd work it out. But I don't see why you'd be less of an outsider than you are here."

"I wouldn't, of course, but I'd be so far outside that I'd be somebody. If I married a faculty member instead of a debased marquis, I'd just be Professor X's sympathetic and helpful wife, which is the same as being the Dean's sympathetic and helpful daughter, which is being nothing but an appendage. I'm trapped in the intellectual world, and I know that if I married somebody on a campus I'd lose my identity entirely. I've watched what happened to my mother, you see. She was a professor's daughter, and she married my father. But she was always an outsider who loved the inside and didn't belong in it, and after forty years or so of it there was nothing left of her. There's nothing worth getting out of bed for. At least in bed she is herself, but it's not much of a self." She paused, and then spoke with great gravity. "I realize I'm trapped. But I can keep fighting against being drowned too. If I can't have a debased marquis at least I can avoid having a faculty member."

"You know your own mind anyway," Nick said faintly.

"Oh, yes. A faculty member would not only be destructive. It would be incestuous."

"What would be incestuous, Marian?" Dean Scarlett had, rather opportunely, completed his clearing up.

Since coming to Acropolis, Nick had fallen into a habit that testified to Acropolis's massive and unsettling effects upon him. His bedtime bouts of introspection were now a regular custom.

This night as usual he regarded the familiar cracks in

the ceiling and contemplated the events of the day. There had been more surprises, but this time some of them offered reverse twists: the surprise of finding Mrs. Overton a familiar and unlikable type in this unfamiliar neighborhood; the mild surprise of learning that Mike Kelly was—or was believed to be—conducting an affair with Mrs. Purview, a rumor that would have been merely routine in other surroundings, just as Mrs. Purview herself would have been routine in other surroundings.

But it was the Scarlett household to which his attention was mainly devoted. Marian and her father were in many ways less uncongenial than most of the people he had met, but in their household they took on a strange coloration, as if the light in Muse Street (from the yellow-shaded lamps) had thrown their personalities into a bizarre chiaroscuro. There was the shadowy and somewhat sinister presence— or more accurately, absence—of Mrs. Scarlett. There was the atmosphere of the parlor, an enveloping atmosphere of withdrawal from the world, of a conservatism that suggested mummification.

Amid that atmosphere Marian moved with vivacity, like a handsome, lively cat that had somehow been imprisoned in a jar of formaldehyde. A woman who showed only half of herself, and that a half that she disdained.

Incest indeed! Nick laughed aloud, not so much at the incongruity of her metaphor as at her determined rejection of the sin. He was uncertain, looking back, whether her statement of principles had been merely another display of mockery or had been intended as a warning.

He was inclined to regard it as a warning. Somewhat gloomily, he conceded that her awareness might be as sensitive as his own. It was possible that she had perceived in him what he had perceived in her, a bewildering and powerful attraction. The warning then was intended only in part for him. She was also warning herself against him.

ONE

In such matters Nick was unself-conscious and realistic.
In considering the fact that a woman found it necessary
to warn herself against him he was not immodest. It was a
familiar situation. What was now uppermost in his mind
was the unpleasant paradox of his position with her. From
her standpoint, he was excluded from any relation with
her because he was a college professor. From his, the more
substantial obstacle lay in the fact that he wasn't.

Suppose she had met not a fraudulent Stuart Hunter but
an authentic Dominic Torrente? He was not a debased
Portuguese marquis, but he met most of her requirements;
at least Dominic Torrente was a wop, an adventurer, a
libertine, and probably, by her standards, debauched.
Against him there would presumably have been no obstacles. What would she have said—or done? And, what was
more to the point, what would he have said—or done?

To these exhilarating questions there were no answers.
So far as he could see, there could never be any answers.

Chapter VI   *Attendance at Classes*

A bell rang.

"Abbott," Nick said firmly. He was gratified to receive an answering noise.

"Allen." Another noise.

"Bablonsky."

"Here," said Mr. Bablonsky.

"Childs."

"Here, sir."

He proceeded to Craig and Cusper and Dosh. In this rhythmic recitation of names there was something faintly soporific, like counting sheep, that intensified his impression of existing in a dream. Or more accurately, in a nightmare, for his condition as he confronted his first class was a fair replica of those disturbing transactions of the subconscious in which the dreamer stands naked on the fully illuminated stage of a large theater, aware that he must perform the leading role in a play that he has never read.

It seemed improbable, Nick detachedly considered, that anyone had ever found himself before in a situation so closely approximating that familiar nightmare.

The theater in this case was a large and dismal hall filled with wooden chairs, each of which possessed a right arm grotesquely enlarged. It was a sort of furniture he had never seen before, and neither it nor the rest of the room did anything to alleviate the symptoms of unreality. At the end facing him the room terminated in a pentagonal projection in each wall of which was set a small stained-glass window, heavily leaded. To compensate for the inadequacy of the daylight admitted by these apertures, one single, powerful bulb had been suspended from the ceiling and encased in a large white globe. The whole effect was that of a billiard parlor casually improvised in an abandoned apse.

The only indication of the actual use of the room was a large and tattered map on one wall, the relic evidently of some long-abandoned cultural project once pursued here. It was entitled Trade Routes of the Hellenistic World, but the colors had faded so that its powers of instruction had become negligible.

The audience before which Nick was to perform his unlearned role was composed of twenty-four faces, incredibly young but sullenly knowing, of devotees of English Composition for Freshmen. "The freshmen," Professor Nutter had told him, "are always the worst." He had wondered at the time in what ways they were the worst; the question was now fully answered. They were, he discerned, the worst in all ways, and they were staring at him fixedly with an unsettling combination of curiosity and apprehension. He attached his glance to the indistinguishable Trade Routes of the Hellenistic World and hoped that he did not look curious and apprehensive himself.

The particular focus of his embarrassment at the moment

was the question of whether to sit or stand. Nobody had given him any information on this point. Nobody indeed had given him any information on any point which would have been of use in his present circumstance, except for Mike Kelly, who told him in a bar a few nights earlier that the important thing in one's first class was not to lose control. "If you lose control of freshmen," Mike had said cheerfully, "you can never recapture it. They all look respectful and shy at first, but if they suspect that you are lacking in authority they become devils. Authority is the important thing."

This advice, which he now instinctively recognized to have been very sound indeed, did not increase his assurance, and Mike had given him no instructions on how to maintain his authority.

There was a platform on which he had concluded he was expected to place himself, and upon the platform was a desk. Behind the desk was a chair, which suggested the propriety of sitting down, but it was possible that it was intended for use only by aged or infirm instructors or in cases of extreme fatigue. To sit in it himself would, he glazedly considered, result in a diminution of authority. The audience looked ominously capable of becoming diabolic at a moment's notice.

To stand, on the other hand, might suggest pretension and even pomposity. It might open so wide a gulf between himself and the seated youths as to encourage them to suppose themselves anonymous or perhaps invisible. And this would certainly lead to disorders and also a diminution of authority. He had compromised by perching on a corner of the desk, suggesting, he hoped, a jaunty casualness and a readiness to spring to a commanding upright position should untoward developments require it.

In this pose of unconcern he reached and passed Milroy and Pasitch, and observed with alarm that he was approaching Weigert. What would happen after Weigert was anybody's guess.

The two dozen faces continued to regard him with menacing expectancy.

The book on the desk beside him provided little material with which he could hope to satisfy any sort of expectations. Its title was *Language and Living: A Textbook of Composition for Colleges*, by Veit, Clapham and Gallagher. He had read it and found it wholly unhelpful. The preface designed for the instructor's guidance was the most unhelpful part of all. It informed him that the authors were seeking to avoid the mechanistic approach of earlier works and that they conceived their purpose to be a furtherance of both analytical and communicational processes among their readers. They stressed the importance of clear, direct English through emphasis upon organizational and expository aspects of writing. Readers were encouraged to deal with "real" subjects (the quotation marks indicating, apparently, a certain lack of confidence about the reality) and even to attempt evaluational appraisals of a critical nature.

The syllabus with which Professor Nutter had provided him, twenty-five copies of which now lay on the desk beside *Language and Living*, was no more helpful. Its rubrics comprised nothing more informative than a series of dates and a corresponding series of cryptic letters and figures which he had with difficulty deciphered. V, C & G 1–14 and Exercise I-b he understood to refer to a portion of *Language and Living*. Excercise I-b was an instruction by V, C & G to "list eight subjects suitable for expository prose statements and prepare a brief epitome of each." But for the present date the rubric contained no instruction except the word "Introduction," which he took to mean some statement of his own rather than of V, C & G. He had indeed asked Professor Nutter what it would be best to say by way of Introduction, and Professor Nutter had seemed flattered by this request for assistance. "Tell them," he had said cordially, "what the course is about and what they're expected to get out of it. Word-Thought nexus, or whatever the psychologists call it now."

Weigert had now been reached and proven present. Nick offered himself a short reprieve by handing out the syllabi. On completion of this task he sat down again on the edge of the desk and observed two dozen faces staring at him. He returned an intent and searching stare of his own.

A searching stare, however helpful as a buttress to authority, could not be indefinitely continued without giving the impression of a paralytic stroke. With nothing to go on except *Language and Living* and Professor Nutter's two sentences, he decided to begin with the more lucid of the latter, and to try to explain what the course was about and what they were expected to get out of it. It now occurred to him that the recasting of this in the form of a question would be likely to delay slightly the necessity of any further statement on his part. He accordingly rephrased Professor Nutter's sentence somewhat impressionistically into four words.

"Why are you here?"

He spoke in a considerably louder and hoarser voice than he had intended, having largely misjudged the acoustics of the room and the effect of extreme nervousness upon his larynx. In fact he fairly bellowed, and the unexpected effect was one of stark drama. As the echoes came to his startled ears, he discerned a resemblance to the manner of President Overton.

This effect was not what he had been seeking, but he was glad to observe that it caused marked, indeed volcanic, responses in the audience. The students quivered slightly and sat bolt upright, regarding him with full attention. Some three-quarters of them merely looked at him. The other quarter, after a moment of startled hesitation, raised its hands.

He had conceived the question as rhetorical, supposing that he would be obliged to follow it by some statement of his own upon the merits of clear, direct English, with emphasis upon its organizational and expository aspects. This obligation could now be indefinitely postponed.

"You, Childs." He pointed at one of the raised hands.

"Well, sir." Mr. Childs was small, untidy, and bespectacled, and his beady eyes bore an expression of distrustful guile. His air of perfect assurance conveyed a hint of insubordination, as if he were using the word "sir" as one might in addressing a wayward dog. "Did you mean here at Parthenon, or here in your class, sir?"

Nick eyed him with a distrust that equalled his own. Here was an established potential devil. "In this class."

Mr. Childs raised his eyebrows.

"Well, sir," he said in tones of languid condescension, "the existence of any systematic intellectual discipline is its own *raison d'être* for serious students."

Among the rest of the class there was a faint stirring, a species of subliminal giggle, which Nick unhappily interpreted as appreciation of Childs. Not of the verity of his proposition, but of the tenuous impudence with which he had uttered it. Something was going to have to be done about Mr. Childs, but Nick at the moment felt himself capable of nothing more authoritative than a resumption of the searching stare. Fortunately another hand now went up. Nick nodded gratefully to its owner.

"We're here to learn to write good," the boy said eagerly.

Mr. Childs regarded this speaker with disdain.

"It seems very unlikely," he began scathingly, "that you will ever achieve that aspiration, judging. . . ."

Nick stood up. The time had come to try to put an end to Mr. Childs, and he essayed to do so with a noise and a gesture—a compelling, wordless monosyllable and an equally compelling wave of the hand simultaneously delivered. It was a technique he had once found effective in quelling a riot in a Bavarian brothel. It combined menace and finality in equal quantities. Mr. Childs subsided. It was evident from his expression that he had not surrendered, but he had certainly retreated.

"When you talk at all, you talk to me." Nick spoke in his most authoritative M.P. manner. "See?"

It looked from their reactions as if they saw. Even Mr. Childs.

"O.K. Now, who else has some ideas?" For the moment his role was familiar. It was that of witness for the prosecution in a court-martial, and he judged that his performance was having precisely the effect he desired. The twenty-four faces regarded him with rapt attention, and, in a few cases, admiration. Another boy put up his hand.

"Milroy?"

"They told us in school you have to study composition before you can appreciate literature."

"Why?" Nick asked, genuinely curious.

"I don't know. That's what Miss Tharp said, though."

Nick considered this. It seemed an unreasonable proposition.

"Please, sir?"

It was Childs again, cowed but not disarmed. With some trepidation Nick nodded to him.

"Fife says that Blake always read the Bible before he wrote a line of poetry."

"Fife? Was that *your* high-school teacher?"

"No, sir." Childs dropped his eyes deferentially. "G. H. Fife, the critic, sir."

"Oh, *that* Fife." Advantage, unquestionably, Mr. Childs. "It would be more interesting if he had said that Blake always wrote a line of poetry before he read the Bible."

There was an unexpected tide of laughter. Advantage Nick. Emboldened, he continued.

"At least that's what you'd expect Blake to do if Miss Tharp is right." He looked at Milroy. "Look, Milroy, don't you think maybe you got it backwards? Maybe Miss Tharp meant you couldn't write well without knowing literature. Like Blake?"

Milroy looked doubtful.

"Well, maybe. I didn't remember it that way, though."

"It seems to me that if that's what she said, she was probably right," Nick went on reflectively. "If you think about it, it has to work out that way, doesn't it?"

They looked at him blankly.

"'I have a dog. His name is Spot.'" Nick was struck by sudden inspiration. The class continued to look at him, not so much with blankness as with interested surmise. "I mean, stuff like that that you learn to write in school. If nobody had ever had a dog named Spot and written it down, then you wouldn't be able to learn to write things like that. If nobody had ever written anything, then you'd never learn to write at all."

A very solemn boy in the front row with black hair, thick glasses, and more teeth than seemed necessary expressed a wish to speak. He did so with an air of pleased approval.

"Then you support the Hecksher-Partch culture-perception thesis, sir?"

"Yes," Nick said austerely.

Another hand went up. A boy with a bad complexion. Cusper, or possibly Dosh.

"But how did it begin? Who did it first?"

A reasonable question, which certainly deserved an answer. Nick felt with some perplexity that in the matter of questions it was much better if he did the asking.

"Well?" He surveyed the class. "How did it begin?"

More hands were raised. He nodded to Mr. Allen.

"Homer," Mr. Allen said.

A reasonable answer. Nick wished he had thought of Homer himself.

"Quite right, Allen. Homer." Mr. Allen appeared gratified. The rest of them wore the persistent look of expectancy, however. It was clear that something more would have to be said about Homer. "As far as literature goes, I guess we can say it started with Homer." He now recalled with fortunate clarity the frescoes on his bedroom ceiling in Rome and the rambling discussion of them that had been conducted by some learned visitors to Lady Tarragon's, fresco-fanciers with a taste for Homeric scholarship or perhaps Homeric scholars with a taste for frescoes. "How Homer happened to start it nobody knows. I've met various characters who know about him. They seem to spend most of their time arguing about whether he existed or not."

He was proceeding at random, aware that a certain percentage of the class was looking rather baffled. It seemed likely that they had never heard of Homer, which was all to the good. Some of the others, however, were giving him knowing smiles in an almost conspiratorial attitude—they presumably had heard of Homer, and that was all to the good, too. The *cognoscenti* appeared to appreciate his brief disquisition on Homeric scholarship, while the illiterate were awed by it. "Personally," Nick continued with some daring, "it seems to me that since he wrote epic poems he must have existed. It's hard to write epic poems when you don't exist."

They laughed.

"Anyway, Homer began it all, and you all ought to read Homer."

One of the illiterates raised his hand.

"Could you tell us the name of the publishers, sir?"

"There are a lot of publishers. The copyright ran out some time ago."

The *cognoscenti* smiled.

"But," Nick went on, "Homer wouldn't help much to find out how the first man to write literature wrote it, unless you read Greek. The people who have translated it mostly don't write as well as Homer."

An illiterate on the second row crossed out with a despairing gesture all the things he had just written in his notes.

Mr. Childs, who had apparently recovered his forces, raised his hand ominously.

"If we are to try to write in the manner of great literature, sir, it would be helpful if you could tell us how to recognize great literature. So that we won't write in the manner of comic books by mistake." Beaten into physical submission, Childs was now transparently determined to outplay his instructor on intellectual grounds. His tones were insinuating, and Nick perceived that his request was a cunning one. No simple answer, even if he had had one at his disposal, would suffice. Some striking display of intellectual virtuosity, preferably buttressed by quotations from G. H. Fife, was required for the devastation of Mr. Childs, and he could discern no possible hope of achieving it. This was obviously the supreme test, for Mr. Childs possessed singlehanded and without question the capacity to transform the rest of them into devils. The singular success of Nick's opening question, his impressive espousal of the Hecksher-Partch culture-perception thesis, all his other successes, were hanging in the balance. He equivocated.

"Quite a lot of comic books nowadays are written by Shakespeare." He paused, and added rather hastily, "So they tell me."

Mr. Childs looked at him with a withering smile. The others, however, remarked the haste in his voice and misinterpreted it. Supposing him to be deliberately suggesting the unthinkable with jocular intent, they laughed. This time they laughed hard. The climate of opinion was, he judged, temporarily anti-Childs and pro-Nick. The issue was still in the balance; he must eventually accept the challenge, but he had gained time. The moment was ripe for another provocative question while he considered plans for the definitive liquidation of Mr. Childs.

"What would the rest of you say? How do you tell the difference between great books and comic books. At least comic books that aren't written by Shakespeare?"

The helpful Mr. Allen volunteered again.

"Well, sir, I'd say it was all a question of art."

It was really remarkable how useful the provocative question was turning out to be. The tables were temporarily turned on Mr. Childs. Nick paused for a moment, but only for effect, before putting the next provocative question.

"What is art?"

This was a good deal more difficult. The class appeared stimulated but hesitant. It was the boy who had expressed a hope of learning to write good who offered to reply. Nick had no great confidence in his power to elucidate the nature of art, but he had no choice but to call on him.

"It's when you paint," the boy said.

"Is that what you had in mind, Allen?" Childs, at whom he glanced covertly while asking, was looking more and more explosive.

"No, sir," Allen said.

"Well, what did you have in mind?"

Allen now assumed an expression of extreme caution. He seemed at first about to say something but evidently thought better of it. There was a difficult silence, but at length two or three of the *cognoscenti* raised their hands, looking as if they were prepared to dispose of Art out of a sense of *noblesse oblige*. Mr. Childs was among them. Nick considered it might be useful to oblige him to deal with these abstruse problems. He realized as soon as he had nodded to him that the impulse was ill-judged.

"I am not interested in casual definitions of art," Mr. Childs said wearily. "I am interested in learning what you regard as the canons of excellence in art."

The moment for the crushing display of intellectual virtuosity had arrived and could not be postponed again. The situation appeared hopeless. But even as he considered its hopelessness, echoes awoke in Nick's mind. The word "canon" evoked certain stirrings, at first inchoate but gradually taking definite form. It was a word Hunter had been fond of, and some of Hunter's coaching now was returning to him. He had not supposed that those dim analyses of contemporary critical tendencies could be germane to the study of elementary composition, but now he saw that they might be handy in disposing of Mr. Childs. And if Mr. Childs were disposed of, English Composition for Freshmen would be entirely manageable. Hastily he assembled from scattered recollections the materials for an essay in aesthetics.

"Contemporary critical canons reject both the Marxist-Formalist standards of the nineteen-thirties and the Neo-Humanism of the twenties," he said to Mr. Childs. There had been no time to explore the possible relevance of the snatches remembered from the *terrazzo*, but it seemed possible that even disconnected items might serve the purpose if delivered with a sufficiently oracular address. Scurrying pencils suggested the accuracy of this guess. His words could not possibly have conveyed any substantial meaning to the note-takers, but even Mr. Childs was bent over his notebook. This was evidently the sort of thing that was expected of an English instructor.

"This rejection may be called the Revolution of the Text," he said in the companionable but authoritative tones of a father explaining the facts of life. "A return to scrupulous concern for the work of art as such, detached from all metaphysics and measurements external to it."

He paused, out of breath and for the moment out of recollections. It would take a little time before he could go on. Resourcefully he rose and wrote the words "Marxist-Formalist" and "Neo-Humanism" on the blackboard. The class studied the blackboard attentively and returned to its notebooks, several of its members crossing out things they had written and inserting revised versions.

"The salient aesthetic purpose of contemporary critics is the perception of—organistic coherence." He produced this phrase with some pride and wrote it on the blackboard, too. Things were not in exactly the right order, he thought, but on the whole the reliability of his memory pleased him.

"Ontology is today the principal element in content study. And if you don't know what ontology is," he went on, observing a satisfactory degree of ignorance on several faces, "I will tell you. It is—" He broke off. He had forgotten what ontology was.

He stood up again and wrote "ontology" on the blackboard while considering evasive tactics.

". . . a philosophical system which, when applied to literature, means . . ."

It would not be reasonable to write "literature," or even "philosophical" on the board. Rapid invention was necessary. "It means," he went on, assuming a tone of profound solemnity, "that the things that a writer is writing about are of less importance than what he has written." He had no grounds for supposing that this was in any way related to the meaning of ontology, but it seemed possible that it might be sufficiently confusing to baffle, or at least delay, systematic analysis.

"In short," he continued hurriedly as if reluctantly winding up, because of pressure of time, a statement that might have been advantageously prolonged for hours, "according to the advanced critical judgment of the day we must apply to all literature the criteria of textural, structural, and tensile analysis."

The pencils rushed over the notebooks, completing the immortalization of these views. Cusper, or possibly Dosh, raised his hand.

"What does that mean?"

It was a good question.

"What does what mean?"

The boy consulted his notes.

"Textural, structural, and tensile analysis."

"'Tensile' means studying—ah—tensions." A phrase, conceivably not wholly applicable, came to his mind. "Acceptance-rejection conflicts," he explained sternly. "'Structural' means the study of structure—that is, the—ah—formal element. And 'textural' means"—the flow of memory had failed completely, and he was obliged to guess desperately at the meaning of textural—"the way a writer actually writes."

This seemed a little anti-climatic. It would be well, he judged, to end with a more rhythmic flourish from Hunter's peculiar dicta.

"We must strive to grasp the unity of the whole together with its accompanying symbol patterns."

He emphasized this final revelation by striking the desk with his fist in what he hoped would suggest a burst of physical and intellectual vigor. In point of fact he was feeling a little tired, although the effect had been, he thought, satisfactory. The class was looking stunned.

"O.K.?" Nick asked amiably.

"O.K., sir," Mr. Childs said a little faintly. It was likely, Nick thought, that there would be no more trouble from Mr. Childs.

"And now we better get down to business." It seemed
expedient to get rid of them as quickly as possible, although
the hour still had some time to run. "Your business is to
learn to write. To write *well.* And the only way to learn to
write is to do some writing. So let's not waste any more
time talking. You better go home and go to work. Writing.
You'll see in the syllabus that you are supposed to do Exercise I-b for next time." He took up *Language and Living.*
"Exercise I-b is to list eight subjects suitable for expository prose statements and prepare a brief epitome of each."

"What does expository mean?" Mr. Cusper asked.

"What is an epitome?" Mr. Pasitch asked.

"But," Nick continued smoothly, "we are not going to do
Exercise I-b. I am going to give you a different assignment.
I want you to write a four-page composition—on—" A
problem now presented itself. In his haste to extricate himself from the necessity of defining expository and epitome
he had embarked upon this new program with no clear
destination in view. ". . . on your attitude toward"—he
hesitated, and said the first word that came to him—"sex."

There was a ripple of applause as the class dispersed.

An interval of one hour was to elapse between English
A and English 49, The Literature of the United States. Nick
devoted it to considering the ordeal just past, reading his
mail, and summoning his resources for the ordeal ahead.

He was on the whole pleased and emboldened by his
experiences with English A. Teaching seemed to be surprisingly easy. All that was necessary was to ask provocative questions in a determined voice and intersperse the
answers, when required, with an occasional show of force
and a few sentences whose absence of exact meaning was
clad in phrases like "organistic coherence." The effects of
this method were gratifying. Incipient rebellion was
crushed. The students, he thought, had enjoyed themselves,

except for Mr. Childs. He felt that his colleagues, and even Stuart Hunter, would approve of his achievements. With a satisfaction verging on smugness he turned to his morning mail.

Since his arrival in Acropolis the only personal item he had received had been a letter from Eugene, Oregon. It had been signed "Clarissa" and had inquired in terms intemperately affectionate but even more intemperately annoyed why Stuart Hunter had not written to her. Clarissa was at some pains to inform Stuart Hunter that if she did not hear from him in the next week she would draw her own conclusions, and that he was to remember that it was he, not she, who had first raised the matter of the salmon swimming upstream.

This unexpected conclusion had provoked Nick's curiosity. He stared at it for some minutes before tearing the letter into small pieces and dropping them in the wastebasket. There was no other action possible, and he hoped that Clarissa would indeed draw her own conclusions.

The rest of his daily mail had been typed, printed, or mimeographed. In the current collection there was as usual a large collection of flyers from publishing houses. He had had no conception that there were so many publishers in the United States, nor indeed that there were so many books being published. He had tended to regard them with dismay, but today he looked at them with approval and even interest as possible means for the discomfiting of future Childses.

THE APE AND THE OCELOT
Bright-orange letters on a shell-pink field. Subtitled: *John Milton and Dorothy Parker: An Adventure in Comparative Criticism,* by Eric Kutz, Assistant Professor of English at Arkadelphia College. A distinguished new title in the HERMES Collection of Critical Studies.

THE GREEN WEASEL

Bright-green letters on a lavender field. Subtitled: *An Annotated Anthology of Twelfth Century Mystery Plays*, by G. Hanscom Emory. A distinguished new aid for your teaching from the VENUS List of Handbooks in Religious Literature.

LITERATURE IN ACTION

Bright-red letters on a black field. By Cormussel, Hacker and Slink. A distinguished new volume in the LYRE Library of College Texts.

Finally a black-and-white announcement, chaste and businesslike, that must have come to him through some mistake in the mailing lists:

A SHORT INTRODUCTION TO LOCAL GOVERNMENT IN SOUTH DAKOTA

As Nick pushed the publishers' notices aside for future consideration, a personal letter, hitherto unnoticed, fell out from among them. It bore an Italian stamp, and Nick recognized the handwriting. Stuart Hunter was corresponding with Stuart Hunter.

Dear Nick [he read],

"I do not know if you are still at this address, but if you have left Acropolis perhaps this letter can be forwarded to you. I have made clear to Diana that she has reason to be concerned about your future, and she has told me I have a duty to try to give you some further assistance in the very difficult—if not impossible—undertaking on which you have embarked. I do not know if this will reach you before you have met your first class. I certainly do not envy you that ordeal. The English Composition, I suppose, you will be able to get by in, but I frankly admire your courage in undertaking to teach an advanced course in American Literature. But as I say, I feel it my duty to do what I can to help you in your undertaking.

"I am sorry we did not have more time to talk about the actual teaching. But under the circumstances it seemed better that you should have some idea, however slight and unsatisfactory, about the literary background. I think now that it would have been more useful to give you the basic rules about teaching, since it is so very easy to make disastrous mistakes, even in the first few minutes of a class, from which one's reputation can never recover. I have seen it happen with several young instructors in courses I have taken myself—and naturally the difficulties of their position were nothing compared to yours!"

Nick eyed the exclamation point with a baleful eye and continued to read.

"This will have to be very brief. The most I can do in this letter is to warn you about some of the more serious hazards. You will probably be tempted by certain classroom practices which seem easy but are intellectually and pedagogically unsound. For example, it is of the utmost importance to maintain discipline, but it is of greater importance still to maintain it subtly. It is only by *demonstrating* the superiority of your mind and knowledge of the subject that you can hope to command the student's respect. From the standpoint of demonstrating your superior knowledge of the field you will, of course, be in a position of serious disadvantage.

"You must avoid showing off. There isn't, of course, much chance that you will be able to do so, so this is not such a serious problem for you as it would be for someone with proper training. Still, you may be tempted to try to impress your classes with big words. Nothing has a worse effect on a class.

"Another thing . . ."

Nick laid down the letter. He had read quite enough of it already, and he was convinced, with a terrible sense of approaching nemesis, that Stuart Hunter's next helpful hint would be against the use of provocative questions.

The rest of his mail was all official, and he began to read it doggedly.

The Registrar, in mimeographed form, urgently requested him to return the enclosed class lists at the earliest possible moment and to indicate on them both given names and, wherever possible, middle initials. In a separate envelope the Registrar requested him to indicate in triplicate his schedule, teaching load, contact hours, and number and names of his counselees, *if any*.

The Dean of the Faculty regretted to inform him that Amos Sisley of the Class of 1903, long a friend and benefactor of the College and a member of the Board of Trustees from 1927 to 1941, had died the previous morning. The Dean of the Faculty asserted his conviction that Nick would wish to attend a Requiem service to be held the following Sunday.

The Bursar informed him that owing to non-payment of fees James Vaux Hooper of the junior class had been excluded from College.

The Provost requested him, by memorandum, to be good enough to concern himself with particular solicitude with the academic comportment of Theodore H. Condon, Jr., a freshman admitted *under special circumstances* who would require the sympathetic assistance of his instructors if he were to maintain a suitable level of intellectual achievement. The Provost reminded him that Theodore H. Condon, Jr. was the son of Theodore H. Condon, '30, of whose many benefactions the Condon Wing of the Gymnasium was merely the latest and most munificent.

The Chairman of the Faculty Committee on the Administration of the Boylston W. Pratt Fund cordially invited him to attend a Recital of Music for Oboe, Bassoon, and Flute, to be performed by the Hamburg Trio.

The Director of Athletics drew his attention to the following members of the Soccer Team who would be un-

avoidably absent from classes on alternate Saturdays during the first semester owing to the exigencies of the Away
Schedule.

On a very smudged sheet printed in purple ink by some
primitive duplicating device, Dave Held of the junior class,
Chairman of the Current Events Forum, informed him that
a Panel Discussion would be held on September 29th, led
by Mr. Morton W. Grasp, Secretary General of the National Institute for Peaceful Relations, on the subject of
United States foreign policy in southeast Asia, under the
title "Worse Than a Crime, a Blunder." Refreshments.

It was at this point that a bell summoned him to his next
class.

The Literature of the United States assembled in a
smaller and less apselike classroom than that which had
contained Composition for Freshmen. Nick arrived at the
last possible moment, morosely hoping that this would
diminish the possibilities for casual conversation with the
students and at the same time add some slight impressiveness to his entrance. For all that he regarded Stuart Hunter
as a fool in every imaginable respect, he could not avoid
the conclusion that the basic message of his letter was
unquestionably correct. The unlikelihood of getting away
with so large a fraud was obvious enough for any fool to
recognize.

He was surprised to find that the room was full. Professor Nutter's discouraging prediction about the size of the
enrollment had been unfounded. There were, as he found
when he read the list of those present, twelve students who
had not been listed for the class. Since he had no idea of
the usual steps for an instructor to take in such a situation,
a frank frontal attack seemed his only choice.

"Who are you all?"

There was a mumble of responses. He sorted out that
eleven of the surplus described themselves as post-regis-

trants while the twelfth, a Mr. Crowe, was, he said, an auditor. Nick was unacquainted with either status, but he supposed that both post-registrants and auditors must be accepted phenomena.

"You've got it fixed up with the right people? It's O.K. for you to be here?"

They nodded. Mr. Crowe was impelled to further explanations.

"I'd have been a post-registrant, too," he said, "but my schedule's full because I've got to make up a math course I flunked last semester. So I'm auditing it, as an extra."

"I see. Why do you *want* an extra?"

Unexpectedly, Mr. Crowe displayed confusion.

"Well, sir, I'm a chem major." He paused, and seemed to conclude that this explanation was not entirely adequate. "They said you were—that is, it would be—good."

"Who said?" The undergraduates had returned to the campus only the day before. Stuart Hunter's reputation must have spread with prodigious speed.

"Well, I heard it," Mr. Crowe said. "Around."

Nick, still puzzled, abandoned the subject out of deference to Mr. Crowe's obvious embarrassment and turned his attention to the larger issues of The Literature of the United States.

Before receiving Hunter's letter Nick had felt less anxiety in approaching English 49 than he had in dealing with Composition for Freshmen. It seemed to deal with more tangible and manageable matters. The Literature of the United States was after all something that could be read. The reading list Hunter had compiled dealt with substantial things, fiction and poetry, and not with such elusive ambitions as the improvement of communicational processes. Nick had read some of the books on the list with interest and certainly with far more comprehension than he had *Language and Living*.

There had, to be sure, been other assignments that Nick had found exasperating. Hunter had proposed to require his students to study long passages from a number of books of critical comment called by such titles as *The Comic Sense in America* and *The Domain of the Objective Correlative*. All these had presented their wares in the same peculiar language that Hunter had used in his efforts to supply Nick with a literary background (however slight and unsatisfactory). Nick had read twenty pages about the Objective Correlative without finding out what it was and then thrown the book across the room and inked out the assignments in it in his syllabus.

The literature of the United States itself, however, had seemed to him smooth and pleasant. In the course of reading quite a lot of it he had accumulated a series of notions that, after addition, subtraction, and clarification, had at last resolved themselves into something that he identified as an idea, or, as Hunter would have put it, a theory— his own theory, the first he could remember having evolved on any subject. Before receiving Hunter's letter, he had proposed to present this theory to English 49 as a sort of introduction to the formidable succession of works that was to extend from the novels of James Fenimore Cooper to that remote moment in May when the students would regale themselves with Ernest Hemingway.

Hunter's letter had unhappily driven the theory entirely out of his mind. In sullen but, he hoped, hidden anger he completed the last details of routine, the handing out of the syllabi.

No alternate plan or project presented itself to him. The sixteen faces regarded him with the now familiar air of expectancy which, though outwardly genial enough, seemed to drive home to him the certainty that the game was up. He could of course simply walk out of that room and remove himself forever from Acropolis. But this, he thought, was precisely what Hunter was anticipating. Instead, with an emphasis increased by his anger, he repeated the question that had so successfully inaugurated the class in Composition for Freshmen:

"*Why are you here?*"

The effects this time were even more striking. The class looked at one another with expressions of delighted satisfaction and a number of hands went up. Cautiously he called on the student who looked to him the stupidest.

"To learn about literature," the boy said.

"What," Nick asked sonorously, "do we mean by literature?"

The class considered. For a disagreeable moment it seemed as if no one cared to offer any views on what we meant by literature. At last another hand was raised. It belonged to Mr. Crowe, the auditor.

"Mr. Pelz said last year in the English Novel that literature was the sum of co-ordinated imagery." He sounded hesitant, even sceptical, as if unwilling to espouse too ardently a controversial thesis that might not commend itself to the current authority.

"And what did he mean by that?"

"What he *said* he meant"—Mr. Crowe sounded more sceptical than ever—"was that a writer turns his ideas into literary effects by imagery, and co-ordinates them in order to achieve—let me see—aesthetic unity, I think." He paused. "I'm not sure I've got it just right."

Right or not, it would do nicely.

"What is imagery?"

Other hands went up. Nick nodded to the volunteer who looked least likely to say anything profound, an oversized, square-jawed young man lounging in his chair and chewing gum. His name, Nick remembered from the Class List, was Untermeister. He looked like Marlon Brando recollected in delirium.

"Imagery," Mr. Untermeister said lethargically, "is the use of images."

"And what are images?"

"Images are pictures," he said after some thought.

There was a slight stirring in the class. Several hands were raised. Nick made a mental note of Mr. Untermeister. It would be profitable to call on him in moments of crisis.

"Images," said the next young man, "are when a writer describes something when he really means to describe something else."

"Like what?"

This seemed to surprise them. There was a distressing lack of raised hands. Nick felt obliged to summon them in hortatory tones.

"Well?" he asked sternly.

"I can't think of any," said the boy who had analyzed images. "Could you suggest one, sir?"

"Water! Water imagery is very common." Nick welcomed his old friend to his support. The class wrote something assiduously in their notebooks. Nick was heartened. "What do you think water could be an image of?" he went on.

This time the response was gratifying.

"The group unconscious," said one student.

"Prenatal fears," said a second.

"Catharsis," said a third, definitely.

"Good," said Nick. "Very good."

The rest of the class energetically took notes on the meaning of water imagery.

"O.K." Nick indicated that the first stage of the discussion was over, and they must pass to more serious concerns. "We've got three different ideas about what water imagery means. How do we know which is right?"

Challenged, they looked at him silently. Even the apostle

of catharsis who had spoken with such assurance appeared doubtful. Presently, however, he raised his hand.

"You try to figure out what the author meant, I guess."

"Is that right?" Nick regarded them with a superior smile. Some gleaning from his random harvest in the field of criticism had returned to him, another thought recalled from Hunter's tedious dissertations—a thought that he privately considered ridiculous but possibly useful now. He answered himself with firmness. "No! It is up to you, the reader, to figure it out. Maybe the author thought that the water was just water, but if he did he was probably wrong. Being wrong about what you think you're doing when you write a novel is Great Art."

The pencils moved with haste, accompanied by a faint but unmistakable flourish of appreciative noises. It sounded as if some of them had heard this thought before but not so well phrased.

"But then how *do* you know?" The apostle of catharsis was persistent. "How can you be sure?"

"Ah," Nick said, pausing impressively while he decided upon a suitable policy. "That is something you will have to figure out during the course of the year. Now," he continued quickly, "in the next week or two you will be reading some books by James Fenimore Cooper. Most of what Cooper wrote was about people operating in forests. Indians and lovely maidens and pioneers. You will notice right away that here is a good example of Forest Imagery. What do you think this Forest Imagery could mean?"

More hands went up. It was really remarkable how eager they were to explain images.

"The group unconscious." This was the same boy who had thought that water was the group unconscious. His preoccupation seemed unwholesome; Nick considered that the moment had come to dispose of it.

"No," he said firmly, "not the group unconscious."

"Well, how about the id?"

"Whose id?"

The boy hesitated. "James Fenimore Cooper's id? Or maybe mankind's?"

"Do you all know what the id is?"

There was no audible response, but ignorance was clearly imprinted on several faces. Nick felt some assurance in dealing with the id. He had heard it explained in Lady Tarragon's salon by distinguished visitors to the point of crushing boredom.

"The id," he said, "is what you would be if you hadn't gotten loused up with evolution and morals." They wrote this down, but some of them appeared unsatisfied. "It is," he went on, "the beast in you. Since you *have* gotten loused up, you repress the id and try to operate as if it weren't there. But it is. O.K.?" Some remnant of perplexity persisted, but he thought there had been enough about the id. "So how do you work out the Forest Image as the id?"

"I guess, sir, that the forest is like the id because it's dark and full of beasts and people are scared of it."

"Including the Indians?"

"No." The young man considered the Indians. "They probably like it."

"Right," Nick said. "They're Id Images."

He was pleased by the neatness with which he had wrapped up the id. "Can you think of something else the forest might be an image of?"

"Capitalism," said an untidy young man briskly.

Nick looked at him apprehensively. There was something in his manner that suggested Mr. Childs. "How do you work that one out?"

"I see the Indians as the victims of capitalist imperialism in the jungle of free competition."

ONE

"A landless proletariat, would you say?" He had heard
a good deal about the landless proletariat in Italy.

"Yes, sir." The young man had clearly moved to Nick's
side. It had been an injustice to compare him to Childs.
"The pioneers are probably the agents of the bourgeoisie."

"What about the lovely maidens?"

"Chattels!" the young man said emphatically. "Nothing
but chattels."

"Ah!" There seemed to be no other comment to make.
"And now, what else could the forest mean?"

"It might be the jungle of American cultural confusion."

"Good. Now let's figure that one out."

The pencils rushed on. An endless series of interpretations of Forest Imagery stretched agreeably before him.
There was nothing to worry about. He moved from the
edge of the desk and sat down in the chair.

At the end of the hour he beckoned to Mr. Crowe as they
left the room.

"I sure liked that, Dr. Hunter," Mr. Crowe said. "Frankly,
it made a lot more sense than when Mr. Pelz tried to explain about literature to us last year. Of course he knew a
lot too, but I didn't get as much out of it."

"Thanks." Nick was genuinely pleased. "I'd like to ask
you confidentially why you and these other characters who
showed up this morning decided to take the course at the
last minute."

"Well, Dr. Hunter, I told you. We kind of heard it was
going to be good."

"How could anybody know what it was going to be
like?"

Mr. Crowe looked at him appraisingly. The official
chasm of rank and learning was very deep between them,
but it was narrow. They were not far apart in age. And
something told them both that they were not very far

apart in tastes and experience either. Mr. Crowe's reticence dissolved. He spoke as a friend.

"Well, some of the boys got together during the last hour. They were talking to the freshmen. The ones in your Composition. The freshmen said it was good. They said you were good at drawing people out." He paused. "They said they felt *challenged*."

"The freshmen said that, did they? They thought it was good?" Nick had been feeling very uncomfortably challenged himself; he did not see why anyone would enjoy the sensation, but clearly the freshmen had meant it as a tribute.

"Yes, sir. Hot, they said. Cool, in fact."

"Thanks, Crowe."

"Yes, sir." Crowe drifted away.

With serene satisfaction Nick found his thoughts wandering to Stuart Hunter. It would be pleasant, he decided, to push Stuart Hunter's head down his throat. It would round off a good morning.

Part Two
THE SECOND SEMESTER

Chapter VII   *Academic Standing*

On a cold morning in February Nick walked briskly across the campus from Theseion Street to Professor Nutter's house on Erechtheion Avenue. It was a Thursday at the beginning of the second semester, and Professor Nutter had expressed a desire to go over Nick's final grades for the past semester.

Looking across the campus, he experienced a faintly startling phenomenon: the view had become by invisible stages familiar, but now for an instant some quirk of his senses presented it to him in the guise of novelty. Fleetingly he saw it as if he were looking on it for the first time. Among the bare branches the contours of the buildings stood revealed, and here he became aware of a further phenomenon. The revulsion they had evoked when he first saw them had faded. Their architectural merits were certainly no greater, but perversely they looked less bleak in the winter setting; their shapes and sizes seemed to harmonize more happily with the frozen lawn and gray sky.

He was thus made aware of the passage of time. A life-time—almost literally—had passed since September, punctuated by landmarks of the academic year. The Matriculation Rite he remembered as he might a happening from childhood. The solemn commemoration of Veterans Day (with the assistance of the Fire Department) and of Pearl Harbor Day (with the participation of a National Guard unit) had grown dim in his memory. The Christmas holiday had come and gone. Now February was running its course. President Overton, it was generally understood, was occupied by preparations for the Feast of St. Matthias, an Apostle whom he had singlehanded designated as patron of Parthenon for no other reason (it was thought) than the exigencies of the calendar. The Feast of Saint Matthias offered almost the only suitable occasion for liturgical and academic display between the Christmas and Easter holidays.

The season was proceeding with no more than a usual dose of drama. There had been a police raid on the Zeta house—and a large black headline in a metropolitan newspaper: "NUDES NABBED IN FRAT ORGY." The frat orgy had been at the beginning of January. It was quickly forgotten, replaced in popular conversation by the apprehension of a student suffering from a peculiar twentieth-century variety of kleptomania whose expensive symptoms took the form of calls to public figures in Tokyo and Buenos Aires secretly made on the private telephones of fellow-students. Then two other students under the influence of alchohol had stolen a police car and so extinguished the stardom of the telephonic miscreant.

Nor had Nick's private life been lacking in incident, although of a sort less sensational and also less public than the frat orgy or the theft of a police car. His private life had come to consist mainly of Marian Scarlett and his relations—for him, at least, as unprecedented as they were unsettling—with her.

He found it surprising that, of all the subjects that had presented themselves to him since his arrival, relations with women, the only one on which he might claim standing as an expert, was the only one he had failed to deal with successfully. But Marian was something new, and she presented the most intractable problem of all. Throughout the autumn they had been meeting, usually for lunch, occasionally in the evening at Muse Street, where he sometimes played backgammon with Dean Scarlett. Their meetings had seemed to take place not as the result of any definite initiative on the part of either of them but rather by a process of spontaneous fusion. In the beginning they had developed out of chance encounters of a sort that occurred almost hourly on the campus, and these had led gradually into the forming of a habit. But they had retained the outward guise of chance encounters—casual, impersonal, and remote. In the course of these ambiguous months Nick had been prepared unwillingly to play her game, standing at arm's length, although her attractiveness remained as strange to him as her resolution to permit no closer approach. But at Christmas an event had taken place, only slightly dramatic in itself and with no outward effect on their subsequent meetings, which yet had involved large and disturbing changes in the terms of their acquaintance.

In Rome, Christmas had not been much regarded, and in those earlier years when its associations and traditions are generally formed Nick had been raised in an atmosphere positively hostile to such celebrations. His early life had been dominated by a view of religious feasts molded during his grandfather's youthful adherence to international anarcho-syndicalism, whose tenets he doggedly observed long after the organization of which he had been

a regional secretary had ceased to exist. This early indoc-
trination in the theory that Christmas was a conspiracy of
the propertied classes had left Nick unprepared for the
lengthy bacchanalia that entwined Acropolis in laurel gar-
lands and decorated Agora Avenue with a procession of
gigantic plastic snowmen. He no longer put any stock in
the ideas of anarcho-syndicalism, but the orgy surprised
him.

And he had not entirely understood what was meant
when the Scarletts asked him to have his Christmas with
them. The phrasing of the invitation, slightly obstetrical in
suggestion, was obscure as well, and he was not at all sure
what was involved. Nevertheless, having nothing else to
do, he accepted. He had already evolved the formula, in
response to questions from colleagues, that it was too far
to go home and that he planned to spend the vacation in
Acropolis. This was not entirely true. In the time between
the end of classes and Christmas Day he visited New
York, expending a striking percentage of the funds saved
from Diana's pay checks and reviving a way of life that
had lapsed since his coming to Parthenon. The brief taste
of familiar relaxations was exhilarating, but he returned to
Acropolis not only with a familiar hangover but with a
quite novel sense of having done some very discreditable
things. He returned, in fact, uneasily aware that during
the three months he had been there the conventional
morality of Acropolis had put its mark on him. It made
him feel old and handicapped, as if a part of his personality had undergone amputation.

Equipped with a bottle of sherry for Dean Scarlett and
one of Scotch for Marian he had presented himself in
Muse Street to find a Christmas tree, a turkey, and a
tendency to sing carols. None of these was exhilarating.
Neither was the gloomy atmosphere of a ritual joylessly
performed. Nick formed the impression that these small

efforts at festivity were Dean Scarlett's idea, and not his daughter's. They composed, he thought, another sacrifice to the altar of the past. He felt sorry for Marian.

Good-naturedly he had accommodated himself to the attempts at Christmas spirit. But he found the atmosphere oppressive, and eventually, when it was beginning to grow dark outside, he had in desperation suggested that a walk would serve as an aid to digestion, and he and Marian had departed together. Then conversation was at first desultory, but it had nonetheless touched on matters of significance.

"It's a dull Christmas for you, Stuart. But it has cheered us up to have you."

He grinned. "I don't mind a dull Christmas after what I've seen of the build-up. I'd rather hear you play carols on the piano than listen to them on a public-address system in Agora Avenue."

"You don't know the words, do you? How did you avoid learning Christmas carols in childhood?" Her voice was a little wistful, as if he must have enjoyed rare opportunities that had been denied to her.

"They didn't approve of them in my family. They didn't go in for Christmas." There seemed to be no particular reason to conceal this fact. It was perhaps less likely that Stuart Hunter's grandfather should have been an anarcho-syndicalist than his own, but it was perfectly possible. She seemed, however, to find his statement uncommonly odd, and she turned to him curiously.

"Your family must have been very—strong-minded. Christmas is hard to resist in America, isn't it?"

"My grandfather was a fighting atheist. And we very very hard up."

"Principle and poverty?" She laughed, cryptically amused by this formula. "A convenient combination. Which came first?"

The question was mocking; he felt himself belittled. These were tender places, and he was the more annoyed for his inability to fight back. His position was undefended and indefensible, and her patronage had suddenly dissolved his good humor. But there was nothing to do except walk on in silence through the cold and cheerless twilight. After an uneasy pause, Marian went on.

"I'd like to hear more about your family," she said thoughtfully. She had left off her mockery; conceivably she was trying to make amends for it. "Perhaps they explain why you are so surprising."

He paused, in an access of prudence. His family background was with Marian and her family the most slippery of subjects. There was no way of telling what information about it might have been provided by Dr. Campion, so dangerously lavish with the provision of information. It was even conceivable that Marian—who might well have been a childhood friend of Clarissa's—might have learned some background information from that source. It might even be conjectured that Clarissa and Marian had corresponded recently on the subject of Stuart Hunter and his misconduct toward that unfortunate girl. He remembered all too clearly Dean Scarlett's conversation on the subject and Clarissa's confirmatory letter.

At this point Nick had stopped suddenly on the path. Here, perhaps, was an explanation of Marian's peculiar attitude toward him. An alarming possibility, but one that had the singular effect of emboldening him to the sort of action he had long resisted. He simultaneously forgot his own reasons for caution, and hers. They had been standing on a path bordered by clusters of evergreens. Now he took her arm, swung her under the shadow of the pines, and kissed her with a determination and a passion that surprised both of them equally.

She had made no resistance, but received his embrace as if she had been expecting it.

"Good evening, Marian. Good evening, Stuart."

The voice from an unnoticed passerby, pausing apparently to admire the view of the pine trees, had interrupted them.

His first reaction to the voice from the path had been reflexive. Such interruptions were not unknown in his previous experience. He had sufficient presence of mind to avoid a sudden, guilty, backward leap, and to restrain Marian from following her inevitable impulse to such a leap. His second reaction was to seek to identify the interrupter, and this had been a matter of no great difficulty. For although the darkening day prevented clear view the greeting had been spoken by a woman with a strong foreign accent. She had, in fact, said, "Goot eef ningue." There was no doubt that it was Mrs. Purview, hurrying in the direction of Stoa Street, who had broken in upon their wintery idyll.

"Jilly," she said.

Nick had permitted himself gradually to become detached from Marian. Despite his disarray, he noted that the cold had made Mrs. Purview's eyes and cheeks glow with fire. She looked more spectacular than ever, and despite himself he felt, as he had when he had first seen her, obliged to forgive the social shortcomings of any woman who looked like this.

"Very chilly," he agreed. "Cold, in fact."

"I do not like this climate. It is damp. In Lithuania we had always snow for Christmas." She was apparently disposed to proceed with light conversation, as if they were meeting at a cocktail party.

Marian, in the shadows beside him, was apparently shocked into total inability to contribute to the discussion, and Nick was obliged to carry it on by himself. He said genially, "We can't choose the climates we'd like."

"I would have chosen to stay in Lithuania," Elsa went on, "if the Germans had not murdered everybody. What times we used to have! The snowballs. The pillow-fights. The drunkenness." She sighed fervently in memory of these lost pleasures of the old regime. "On Christmas Day, the grownups always made love in the snowdrifts."

"Very nice," Nick said.

"Here it is too damp to make love outside in winter. One must go in the house."

"Merry Christmas, Elsa," Nick said with finality.

She hesitated. Nick had already taken Marian's arm and was steering her in the opposite direction, but as they commenced their retreat, Elsa continued. "There is the danger of catching cold in this dampness," she called after them.

"Merry Christmas," Nick said again. He propelled Marian rapidly away, and in a moment Elsa had disappeared into the twilight.

"She is a real lunatic," Marian said, after a moment's lapse, in a somewhat stifled tone.

"It was nice of her to warn us about catching cold, though."

Marian ran her hand through her hair, staring at him. Mrs. Purview had decisively ended the idyll; there was no doubt of that. She had also, oddly, illuminated its meaning. There could be no doubt in either of their minds now that beneath the decorous and dispassionate months before there had lain something a great deal larger than casual attraction, but the interruption had recalled Nick to a realization of his false and precarious position; and for Marian it seemed to have re-emphasized an even greater inhibition.

"If you'd rather stop seeing me, Stuart, I shall quite understand. But this mustn't happen again."

"Why not?"

"Elsa."

"Elsa?"

"She's on her way to Mike Kelly's, you know."

"I suppose she is. What of it?"

"I couldn't bear that kind of thing. The endless gossip. The furtive meetings. The futile attempt to—escape."

"What from?"

"If I am going to get away from Parthenon, it must be a clean break. Not a gossipy affair with an instructor. If I let you think we can go on as anything except acquaintances, I'd be guilty of false pretenses. And false pretenses are the one unforgivable crime, Stuart."

For Nick the words had cut very deep. For one taut moment he had hesitated on the verge of a full confession and then the word "Stuart" had revealed its folly. He was caught in the inescapable trap. An instructor was unacceptable. And Nick Torrente, considering the circumstances of his presence, would be more unacceptable still, in view of her feelings about false pretenses.

The hell, he had suddenly thought, *with her feelings about false pretenses.* Or about anything else. The recurrent sense of imprisonment that had sent him to New York the week before now abruptly came to include resentment against the restraints that she was imposing upon him.

They had walked back in silence. Later he had disciplined himself—or, more precisely, surrendered to the need for discipline that his impulses demanded—to renew his meetings with her on the basis of acquaintanceship. But a strong sense of bafflement, punctuated by fits of rage, persisted.

But if his private affairs were unsatisfactory in the extreme, his professional career was flourishing. He was still on excellent terms with his Acting Chairman. If anything a shade too excellent, for Professor Nutter's attitude toward him was disconcertingly proprietary. Still, he felt he had nothing to fear from that affable scholar. Moreover, his assurance about his own capacity as a teacher had progressed very considerably. He had successfully composed, administered, and graded the mid-semester examinations, and he had forgotten the days when the word "mid-semester" was wholly cryptic to him. Now, having dealt with final examinations as well and commenced the work of the second semester, he was sure that Professor Nutter would approve the grades he had given.

He had grown a great deal more assured about the study of literature. He had just delivered a stirring lecture on Guilt Themes in Hawthorne, an author for whom he felt a particular affinity. His knowledge of critical vocabulary had broadened almost as rapidly as his knowledge of literature. He was no longer confined to water and forest imagery. Two days before he had lectured for a full hour on the subject of Romance in America, referring twice to the concept of the monomyth and once to euhemerism. His lecture had been lavishly studded with references to Authorities, only one or two of whom he had had to invent to meet his needs. He had controverted, at some length and with total confidence, the assertions of a Mr. Progmore, a junior with literary pretensions, that Hester Prynne was to be construed as the Earth Mother.

He felt, in short, no great doubt about his ability to teach convincingly. It even seemed to him possible that the students were learning something. Not perhaps from him, but at least from the works that he and they were reading together. And in this regard he had one large advantage over the students: he could read faster.

In spite of these reassuring achievements, there was still

cause enough for anxiety. For one thing the thought of Stuart Hunter periodically haunted him. There had been more letters, and Hunter's favored opening sentence was, "If you have still managed to avoid exposure . . ." He had grown hardened to these messages and to the spectral threat associated with them, but he still disliked them very much. And he disliked even more the uninformative acknowledgments that he felt compelled to write from time to time, in the belief that a mysterious silence on his part might excite an unwholesome spirit of exploration in Rome. This anxiety had, to be sure, lately subsided. For some time he had had no letters, but a mysterious silence on Hunter's part was also in its way disturbing. He was apprehensively ignorant of what was going on in Hunter's mind now.

More immediately, he was still perpetually beset by crises arising from his own fraudulence. Every day, in the course of conversations with his colleagues or dealings with the administration, intricate problems developed, arising mostly from strange words and practices. The supply of strange words and practices in academic life appeared inexhaustible, and his hardest problem was his inability to distinguish those that were supposed to be familiar to any educated person from those that had a peculiarly local currency.

His most alarming conversations were with his fellow-scholars of literature. With Mike Kelly, or Brandon Craig, he generally felt on safe enough ground—like everyone else on the campus they displayed an almost ritualistic respect for the privacy of another man's specialty. But with Dr. Pelz and Dr. Shalcross he frequently found himself in trouble. They were unpleasantly disposed to discuss literature.

"Do you feel," Dr. Pelz had asked him one day, "that there is anything in Schrift's idea about the common symbol patterns in Dostoevski and Louisa May Alcott? It's the line he took in that article in the N.E.C.P.A. two years ago." Still more unnerving had been a casual question of Shalcross's: "Do you really think that Herbster made sense in that last article on Bardic elements in Hopkins' prosody?" This was disturbing not because Nick had never heard of Bardic elements but because he had heard of Herbster. Herbster had been one of Hunter's supervisors in graduate school, and he was expected to produce some background information about him even if he disavowed knowledge of the prosody article.

These dilemmas he had so far parried with footwork. They remained, however, a standing source of anxiety. So did some of the little chores set him at intervals by Professor Nutter. "Just run over to the Registrar's office," Professor Nutter would say, "and check the transcript on Mr. Glueberry to see if he has completed his Semantics prerequisites." But he had always managed to find his way around through the forests of transcripts and prerequisites and standing requirements without fatality. And each day brought clarification of some mysterious phenomenon like mid-semesters.

On the whole, it was in good spirits that he rang Professor Nutter's doorbell.

"Good morning, Stuart," Professor Nutter said cordially.

"Yes, sir."

"They are," Professor Nutter said, showing him into the living room, "at it again."

"Are they indeed, sir?"

"Yes. I just went to Barrowes to get my mail. I saw him go in."

Nick was now sufficiently versed in Professor Nutter's preoccupations to guess at the meaning of this cryptogram. He judged that Professor Nutter had seen Professor Woodbine, the apostle of Semantics, on his way into the President's office, and that Professor Nutter believed them to be up to no good. "What now, do you think, sir?" he asked.

"Babcock," Professor Nutter said darkly.

"Babcock?" His cryptanalytical skills were insufficient to this. It seemed possible that babcock was some Nutterian variation on poppycock, but there was no way to be sure.

"He was going in too. He's just gotten back from abroad."

"Oh," Nick said.

"Switzerland. I don't like the looks of it. What would Babcock and Woodbine be doing there together?"

"I don't know."

"I don't trust trustees," Professor Nutter said. So Babcock was a trustee. "They meddle," Professor Nutter went on. "Especially Babcock. Geopolitics!"

"Geopolitics, eh?"

"He's been at this game for years. In 1938 he went to Germany, and then he gave the college a geopolitician."

Nick laughed.

"I knew you'd agree," Professor Nutter said, smiling. "Absolute rubbish, of course. Babcock thought he was wonderful. Kleinwelt. From Halle. Or possibly Marburg. He left after one semester fortunately. But Babcock keeps trying. The President encourages him. And Woodbine too, of course. The latest fads. This time it may be choreography. Or space travel. Traction!"

The last word seemed out of place. "Traction?" Nick asked.

"Buses, all over central New York State. He's made millions so he can afford to meddle. Now, as regards this matter, we have a curve."

"For the buses?"

"Only for the introductory course," Professor Nutter went on. Nick realized that a transition had been made, and they had entered upon a discussion of the semester marks. "You didn't know that?"

"No, sir," Nick said.

"Nobody ever tells me anything, either," Professor Nutter said vaguely. "Fifteen, thirty-five, thirty-five, fifteen. But only as a general proposition. Over a period of years."

He had uttered this obscure statement with his usual emphasis, and was now looking at Nick questioningly. Nick resorted to his favorite solution.

"Well!" he said.

"Will you come out as fifteen, thirty-five, thirty-five, fifteen? Approximately, of course?"

"I don't know what I'll come out as, sir," Nick said honestly.

"No, I wouldn't expect you to," Professor Nutter said genially. "Not if they didn't explain to you first. Let us add them up."

Professor Nutter held out a hand expectantly, obviously for the rollbook containing his class records which Nick was holding. He handed it over. Professor Nutter opened and studied it intently, jotting down figures as he read.

"I figure twelve and a half, twenty-five per cent, forty-five and a half per cent, roughly, and, counting the D and the E's together as we must, twelve and a half per cent. Not too bad in itself. Better than Shalcross. Or Pelz. It's only a general proposition, of course. Over the years. Clayfoot," he added musingly, "never paid any attention at all to the curve. Pelz was Clayfoot's man."

"I see, sir." It was true. The role of the curve still escaped him, but Nick had grasped the general situation.

"It will do, Stuart, it will do well enough. Who were the failures?"

"Cusper and Condon, sir. They are stupid."

"Condon? And Cusper?"

Nick uneasily noticed an unwonted interest in Professor Nutter's voice.

"Cusper and Condon, eh?" Professor Nutter repeated

inscrutably. He continued to study the list, his head bent
backward to afford a more convenient view of the rollbook
through his bifocals, a position which made him appear
more birdlike than ever. "And what else have we? A D for
Childs. Hmm."

He straightened his head and looked at Nick.

"Childs and Condon," he said, "are very well thought
of by the Provost. Their fathers are trustees. Childs is supposed to be a genius."

"He's a disciplinary problem," Nick stated emphatically.
He hesitated, and judiciously added, "Too."

"I'm delighted, my boy. Absolutely delighted. Old
Childs was behind that move to abolish the literature
requirement. The time Miss Armstrong went to jail for
embezzling. They're always meddling."

Nick was too greatly relieved to wonder whether the
connection between the literature requirement and Miss
Armstrong's embezzling could be more than chronological.

"And now, let us have a look at the other lists. Ha. A D
Minus for poor Untermeister."

"Yes, sir. He's stupid, too."

"A D Minus is generous for Untermeister," Professor Nutter observed. "I failed him in the Renaissance."

He continued his analysis. Somewhat to Nick's surprise,
he did not challenge any of the marks. His interest was
that of a sporting enthusiast surveying the latest results.
"So Kaprovitch only got B—a pity. He is one of our most
promising majors. I have hopes of Phi Beta Kappa. But
then, perhaps American literature is not his best subject."
He spoke a little wistfully, as if he had backed a favorite
who did poorly on a muddy track. "Abercorn, E," he continued. "Admirable, my boy, admirable. He went to St.
Mark's. I am always glad when boys of good family do
badly. The President would like to fill up the college with
them."

There seemed to be no foreseeable pattern to Professor Nutter's prejudices. But since they clearly included a strong prejudice in favor of himself Nick accepted them cheerfully.

The business session drew to its close, which was marked by Mrs. Nutter, bearing a tray with coffee and homemade cookies. It was the standard form of entertainment among the Parthenon faculty, being cheap and easy and providing opportunities for courteous remarks along lines of, "Did you really make these nutmeg crisps yourself, Mrs. Nutter?"

"Did you," Nick asked, "really make these nutmeg crisps yourself, Mrs. Nutter?"

"They turned out badly," she said with her accustomed grace. "The salt got in."

It had indeed. "Delicious," Nick said resolutely.

"They taste terrible," Mrs. Nutter replied. "They're better than Hattie Hammersmith's though. She uses margarine."

"You never knew old Hammersmith, of course?" Professor Nutter asked.

"A crab," his wife said. "It's a good thing he died when he did. Otherwise—" She stopped, endowing the truncated sentence with really appalling implications.

"He was in philosophy," Professor Nutter explained, suggesting by his somber tone that old Hammersmith had succumbed to a protracted immersion in it. "He drank."

"*Drank?*" Mrs. Nutter indicated the utmost disdain for the feebleness of the term. "You say drank. Any sensible person would say that he was a hopeless alchoholic. He saw things." She laughed harshly. "Epistemological dualists, mostly."

"They chased him up and down Stoa Street one night," Professor Nutter said. "With no clothes on."

Nick felt, as was so often the case in his conversations

with the Nutters, as if he too had been drinking. "The epistemological dualists had no clothes on?"

"No, no." Mrs. Nutter was impatient. "The epistemological dualists were painted bright blue, he said afterward, and had tails. It was Hammersmith who had no clothes on. He died as a result."

"Well, Lovecake, they said it was mostly cirrhosis. Exposure was only a precipitating cause."

"Nonsense. He got pneumonia. Hattie told me so. His liver was perfectly all right."

"He was one of the President's appointments, of course. It's hard to see how he could have made a worse one."

"You're crazy, Fred," Mrs. Nutter said, adding another to the rather numerous points on which Nick had, through the months, found himself in agreement with her. "There are worse things than drink."

Professor Nutter was sceptical. "What, Peach Blossom?"

"Are you forgetting Hindmire?" She sounded triumphant.

"Well, yes, Hindmire."

"A shocking case," Mrs. Nutter said. "Outrageous."

"I don't believe I've heard about it," Nick said boldly.

"No, of course you haven't. We never mention his name."

Professor Nutter chewed lengthily on a nutmeg crisp and was silent. Nick remarked with surprise that for the first time Professor Nutter was reluctant to discuss a Parthenon scandal. The Hindmire case must certainly have been of a monstrous nature.

"It's time he heard about it," Mrs. Nutter said. "He's sure to hear sooner or later. Anyway, it concerns the Department." She turned to Nick. "Everybody knew about it of course, although Clayfoot tried to keep it quiet."

"Just what you'd expect of Clayfoot," Professor Nutter said. "He tried to protect Hindmire. His eyes were always blinded when a young man was popular with the students.

Most popular teachers are bad teachers," he observed sententiously. "Scandalous. Absolutely scandalous." Despite the severity of his words, his voice carried the tenuous suggestion of a chuckle as he added surprisingly, "Harvard!"

"Harvard is scandalous?" Nick asked.

"No, no." Professor Nutter beamed. "He failed. Twice."

"He was bound to fail," Mrs. Nutter said austerely.

"Twice," Professor Nutter repeated.

"What did he fail?" Nick asked.

"Generals. Twice."

"That wasn't the worse of it," Mrs. Nutter said. "Tell him."

"The worst of it, Stuart, was that he lied about it. Repeatedly."

"He lied about failing generals?"

"He said he'd passed them."

Although not absolutely certain about the nature of generals, Nick stared at them with a sudden feeling of sickness.

"There have been several young men," Professor Nutter went on, "in other departments of course, who had failed their general examinations when they were trying to finish their degrees. That's why I prefer a young man like you who has finished his degree. But if they fail, it's merely discreditable. Hindmire *said* he'd passed. Then he said he'd finished his dissertation and gotten a Ph.D. from Harvard."

"He said he had a Ph.D. when he didn't?"

"Exactly."

"They put it in the catalogue," Mrs. Nutter said. "Edgar Hindmire. Ph.D., Harvard. It was nauseating."

Professor Nutter nodded. "Clayfoot had been going to promote him. He was one of Clayfoot's favorites. Of course, he had to leave immediately. I always suspected Clayfoot would have liked to keep him on, but even the President saw that was out of the question. Absolutely inexcusable conduct. Sad of course. I was delighted."

"Delighted?" Nick could only repeat this unexpected word.

Professor Nutter smiled broadly. "Native songs and dances. Utterly unreliable. I couldn't bear the fellow. Native songs and dances *on the desk*. I saw him. Jumping up and down on the desk. Through the window in Xenophon 12. He said afterward he was illustrating the structure of *Pride and Prejudice*."

Nick was judicious. "It seems pretty unlikely."

"Very unlikely. But the students like that sort of thing. They adored Hindmire. Beer parties."

"Say what you mean," Mrs. Nutter said to her husband. "Nobody ever knows what you're talking about."

"He gave beer parties for them. And *went* to beer parties. At the Houses. Including," Professor Nutter lowered his voice, "the Zeta House. He courted popularity."

"Oh," Nick said.

Professor Nutter smiled beneficently. "Courted it. A favorite of Clayfoot's. Always trying to outshine everyone else, and Clayfoot encouraged it. He was always encouraging the younger men."

"He had to learn," Mrs. Nutter added. "Just as Hindmire had to learn he couldn't get away with claiming he had his degree."

"Why *didn't* he get away with it?" Nick tried to keep his voice from rising. "How did they happen to find out that he didn't have a Ph.D.?"

"Well." Professor Nutter was absolutely jubilant now, and so, judging from her expression, was his wife. "*I* found out. No one else would bother looking into it. I always thought there was something wrong with him. A sound man doesn't go to beer parties with students."

"How did you do it?"

"Research, my boy. I simply applied scholarly methods. I happened to find myself in the library one day near the shelf where the university catalogues are kept. I looked up the Harvard list of degrees granted. Hindmire's name was not there. I won't say I was surprised."

"You suspected him?" Nick asked. "You thought there was something suspicious about him?"

"Oh, yes. Very definitely suspicious. I could tell at a glance he was not a real scholar. I always can. Clayfoot never noticed anything of course."

"Well!" Nick's voice faltered.

"I thought you'd agree." Professor Nutter took another nutmeg crisp.

Nick felt a strong impulse to remove himself from the presence of the Acting Chairman. A need for solitude had been rapidly growing. "I guess I better be going."

"Have another nutmeg crisp," Mrs. Nutter said hospitably. "And some more coffee. You've hardly touched yours. I suppose you don't think it's good."

"Delicious." Nick gulped. "But the conversation has been so interesting—to hear about Hindmire." At the risk of confirming his hostess's suspicion that he didn't like her coffee, he got to his feet. "Delicious," he said again enthusiastically. "And the nutmeg crisps."

"Take some home with you. I'm glad to bake for young bachelors—like you." Mrs. Nutter was positively coy, and as he turned to thank her, she contorted her large, soft face into a wink. "I'll wrap them up. They're a lot better than Hattie Hammersmith's."

Nick went out, bearing a parcel of nutmeg crisps, and walked toward the campus.

He was more than shaken. Professor Nutter was a far greater danger than he had dreamed, and his own relations with him not as certain as they had seemed. At the moment Nutter's regard for him was that of a man for some cherished piece of personal property. He had evidently forgotten the disagreeable fact that it was Clayfoot who had hired Stuart Hunter, but if any rumors of Nick's social life—which included a good many dinner parties as well as occasional visits to the Zeta House—reached him he might well remember it. Indeed, any substantial indications of popularity with faculty or students—even, it seemed, any indications of an independent existence—might divert his approval into hostility and thence to malicious research.

The aspect of the Hindmire situation at once most disturbing and most curious, then, was the problem of what had first provoked Professor Nutter's suspicions and led him fatally to the Harvard catalogue. Had there been something odd in Hindmire's conduct that suggested a fraudulent degree? Had he proved ignorant of some Masonic formula, known only to doctors of philosophy, whose lack must, in time, become evident? Or was it merely that Professor Nutter's jealousy and dislike had been provoked by injudicious conduct on Hindmire's part? Nick thought he could, with difficulty, protect himself against such imprudence. But against the former sort of difficulty there was no defense.

He felt a compelling urge to find out more about Mr. Hindmire, or at least to hear another version of his downfall. The best, if not the only, person from whom to seek information was Marian. It was nearly lunchtime, and since they often lunched together it would be natural enough to suggest it today, and to raise the question of the scandal that no one ever mentioned. He turned toward Barrowes Hall.

As he approached her desk, she looked up and said, "Ha."

Nick started. He was in no mood to have people saying "Ha" to him. "What's the matter?"

"I have something important to tell you. I'm glad you came by."

"What?"

"I said I'm glad you came by."

"No. What have you got to tell me?"

"It's rather involved, and it may raise some serious problems."

"Great!" he said.

She was startled by his gloomy emphasis. "I can't go into it right now. The President has some things for me to do."

"I was going to ask you to have lunch."

"Fine. I shouldn't be long."

"I'll wait for you outside." He felt that another dose of winter air would be helpful, and he turned to the door, resenting this tendency of portents to accumulate.

Chapter VIII   Student Publications

*N*ick waited impatiently on the steps of Barrowes Hall
for Marian to come out. There had been something in her
manner that perturbed him, something about her pregnant
"Ha" that suggested some seriously alarming news. He was
anxious to question her about Hindmire, but Hindmire
was slightly effaced from his anxieties by the prospect of
her forthcoming revelations.

The morning's events had left him in a preternaturally
sensitive state of mind. He was now ready to read suspicion into the most routine events, while in the past he had
been more struck by Parthenon's credulity than by its
scepticism. He had sometimes been embarrassed by what
he regarded as displays of trusting acceptance; he wondered now if they had not been merely a cloak for an
unpleasant tendency to divert scholarly training into paths
of criminal detection.

As he waited, the inmates of Barrowes Hall began to

emerge for lunch, and as they emerged they paused to chat in a fashion that was habitual with them, as with everyone else at Parthenon. This morning Nick approached such familiar conversations warily, and with deep suspicion. The first to come out was the Bursar, Mr. Freeman, an austere man who looked, like somebody unwillingly employed as a keeper in a Big Cat House, as if his heart were not in his work.

"Good morning, Hunter," he said. "You have, I believe, been teaching a freshman named Thrope?"

"Yes, I have."

"Would *you* say he was scholarship material?"

The question sounded like a trap. With some effort, Nick summoned his powers of rational discourse, wishing that he knew precisely what was meant by scholarship material.

"Well . . ." he said.

Mr. Freeman eyed him narrowly. "It is difficult, of course, to appraise scholarship material. Particularly for those who are not very *experienced*. But I should like to hear your judgment."

"He got B Minus."

"Marks," Mr. Freeman said, eying him more narrowly still, "are not everything. There are impalpable requirements."

It sounded remarkably like a test of some sort. "Of course," Nick said. "I'd say he had them."

"Ah, you would, eh? The physicists don't think so."

Mr. Freeman's features darkened, and he moved on, waving a noncommittal gesture of farewell. It was hard to tell whether he agreed with the physicists or not. There was no substantial indication of scepticism in his manner, but his questions struck Nick as sinister. It was with heightened apprehension that he greeted Mr. Cannon, the next of the administrators to come out.

Unlike Mr. Freeman, his manner was cheerful. Mr. Cannon was Director of Development, and it was his responsibility to raise money, in contrast to Mr. Freeman, whose job was to pay it out.

"I bet," Mr. Cannon said with a smile so sunny as to appear factitious, "you don't know how I spent last night."

"No, sir."

"*At the deathbed of Arthur Chiswold Garth!*"

To this revelation, uttered with triumphant glee, Nick could think of no reply whatever. He was inclined to suspect some dark, fraternal code.

"Of the Class," Mr. Cannon went on, "of 1905. You know, of course, about Arthur Chiswold Garth?"

"Well, yes and no."

"It all turned out most satisfactorily."

"You mean he didn't die?"

"On the contrary, on the contrary. I am thankful to say that the end came at seven this morning. He lost consciousness at midnight, but I felt it my obligation to stay. At eleven he had signed the codicil. My timing was perfect. I think," he continued with even greater jubilation, "that I need not tell you what this will mean to all of us. I count it my best night's work since I blackmailed old Murdock's widow."

"Since what?"

A very faint frown dispelled some of Mr. Cannon's sunniness. It seemed possible that he felt some slight doubt about the discreetness of his phrasing. But doubt dissolved in his buoyant satisfaction at the thought of Mr. Garth's codicil. "I happened to find out once—years ago this was —that old Murdock had plagiarized several passages in his translations of Plautus. I was just leafing through them— making a comparative study with some other translations, you might say." He paused, perhaps feeling that this was implausible. "I try to keep up with the scholarly writings of the faculty. And I found that old Murdock had lifted a number of key passages. I felt, of course, that his widow ought to know about it. She was enormously wealthy."

Despite the sunniness of Mr. Cannon's manner, Nick felt a distinct chill. "Who was this Murdock?" he asked.

"A classics man. Many years ago," Mr. Cannon said. "In any case, I had a little talk with his widow. And in the course of it, she generously agreed to make a gift to the college. Naturally," he added jovially, "I was joking when I used the word blackmail."

"Naturally," Nick said. "And what made you think it might be worthwhile to compare his translation with the others?"

"Instinct," Mr. Cannon said airily, perceiving that his indiscretion had provoked no reprobation. "You develop an instinct about these things. Well, I'm off to take a nap. You don't get much sleep in my line of work."

And Mr. Cannon wandered happily away.

He was immediately replaced by Dr. Kilmote, of the Physics Department.

"Hello there, Hunter," Dr. Kilmote said. Like Mr. Cannon, he appeared to be in excellent spirits. "I have just had a most gratifying discussion with the Provost."

"Good," Nick said. He was brooding on Mr. Cannon's instinct for the unmasking of scholars who plagiarized, and he felt no great interest in Dr. Kilmote's discussion with the Provost.

"He has approved the new equipment. In principle."

"That's fine."

"For the B and G lab."

"Great."

"It has been a disgrace. But with the new equipment, I think we shall have something to attract a new man we're looking at." Dr. Kilmote was talking on dreamily, a characteristic, Nick had noticed, of physicists. They rarely seemed aware of the exact identity of the person they

were talking to. "A most promising man from California.
I have been going into his credentials very carefully. I am
always extremely careful to investigate credentials."

"What do you do, exactly, when you investigate credentials?"

"I found nothing to arouse suspicion in this case. And
with the new equipment I think he will find our offer
attractive. He will be able to continue his own work in B
and G. The y reaction looks very promising."

"How can you be sure," Nick said, "that he's so hot on
B and G?"

"I am confident that he's the man we think he is," Dr.
Kilmote continued vaguely. "Nice to talk to you, Hunter.
I knew you'd be interested."

Dr. Kilmote drifted away.

In the few minutes that now elapsed before Marian's
appearance, Nick's thoughts made a quite unwonted approach to panic. A reasoned appraisal of the transactions
revealed by the Messrs. Freeman, Cannon, and Kilmote
might suggest nothing more than a series of mild coincidences, but in Nick's present state of mind coincidences,
however mild, were converted at once into a pattern of
doom. The three amiable gentlemen appeared to him in
the guise of nemesis.

Taken in conjunction with the Hindmire case and with
Marian's unsettling statement, they induced a slightly cat-
atonic state, and his subconscious added to it by the pro-
duction of still more alarming materials. His mind, travers-
ing the subject of scandals, came to rest in the Zeta House.
The headline recurred to him: "NUDES NABBED IN FRAT
ORGY." Other headlines now formed themselves gratui-
tously on the horizons of consciousness. "PROF BARED
AS PHONY: CAMPUS ROCKED" . . . "FAKE PH.D.
STIRS CRISIS" . . . Or even, "LYNCHING LOOMS IN
PARTHENON EXPOSÉ."

It was in the course of these vaporous imaginings that Marian appeared, and by reason of them he greeted her with a brusqueness that startled her.

"What is all this?" he asked without preface.

"All what?"

"This important thing you have to tell me."

"Important, but not urgent, Stuart." She looked at him questioningly. "And in any case, confidential. I'll tell you when we get to lunch."

They walked across the campus to Agora Avenue and their habitual luncheon resort, a restaurant that bore in neon letters six feet high the words "ACROPOLIS EATS," though whether as a name or a statement of fact was not clear. When they were seated in a booth, Nick said explosively, "Now!"

"You seem distraught," she said calmly.

"Go ahead, tell me what it's all about."

She looked at him enigmatically, and then rose slightly from her bench to look into the adjoining booths. Satisfied that they contained no eavesdroppers, she sank back and turned her attention to Nick with an air of cryptic detachment. "This is something very big," she said importantly.

"So you keep saying. What is it?"

"Probably I oughtn't to be telling you at all, but I think you'd better know. As I said, it may raise some serious problems."

"Yes. I remember. What are they?"

"What's the matter with you today, Stuart? Are you ill? Or have you a guilty conscience?"

"Guilty conscience," he said, a little thickly.

"You ought to conceal it better. However, this is something you needn't feel guilty about. In fact, you ought to be pleased."

"You said it would raise serious problems. I wish you'd stop being mysterious."

"Irritable as well," she said blandly. It was evident that his impatience had provoked in her an impulse to mischievous prolongation of the preliminaries. She was, he noted with the half of his mind that was still capable of detached operations, very like her father in some ways. "It's highly confidential, and still tentative. I really oughtn't to be telling you at all."

"Oh God, Marian."

"It's the big news about the *Achaean*."

"The what?" The word conveyed to him at the moment only the haziest of associations, and those, identified after a second's thought, were with Homer, who seemed of unlikely relevance to the circumstance of Big News.

"The *Achaean*. You've heard of it?"

"Oh." Another association, more germane to current events if not noticeably more applicable to his own condition, occurred to him. "The yearbook."

"Yes. It goes to press, you know, before the Easter vacation, so they have to get everything ready now."

"That's interesting."

"It seems to me very dull. But what is interesting is that they've had their elections."

He nodded, aware that the yearbook annually conducted a poll in which undergraduates voted for the most likely to succeed, and similar distinctions, among their number.

"The returns aren't quite all in as I understand it," Marian went on, "but there are already some landslides. Teddy Untermeister brought the results in to Father." She paused, again provocatively, but he understood nothing of what she intended to provoke. "Do you know Teddy?"

"Untermeister? Yes, he's in one of my classes. A lout."

"Yes, he is rather. A campus figure, though. He was a great athlete until he was disqualified. They've a rule that you can only play for four years. He's been here several more than that. But he had so much prestige as an athlete that they made him editor of the *Achaean*. As consolation I suppose. In any case he came in to show Father the election results. Father goes over everything they publish in the yearbook."

It was more and more evident that these enthralling facts were being intended as moves in a conversational gambit designed to provoke still greater impatience on Nick's part. He tried with partial success to remove the grounds for such provocation. "That's good," he said absently.

"It is sometimes rather delicate, of course. As you know, people pay a good deal of attention to the election results. They used to vote for the most unpopular member of the senior class as well as the most popular, but Father made them stop. It upset people's parents. I'm told that they still do some clandestine poll-taking on the side, about subjects not suitable for publication, and circulate the results privately. But that's beside the point. The point is that, as you know, they also express their opinions on the faculty."

"That's interesting."

"No it isn't." It was Marian who was impatient now. "Why do you keep saying things are interesting?"

Nick shrugged his shoulders in a demonstration of un-interest.

"But the *results* are rather interesting this time according to what Father indiscreetly told me. You realize, no doubt, that everyone is expected to await the results in a state of breathless suspense, so it was very indiscreet of Father to talk about it before anything was definite. Do you know who the Most Popular Faculty Member is?"

"No."

Marian looked thoughtfully at the table. "You."

He gulped.

"And do you know whom they've voted the Best Teacher?"

"Not Stuart Hunter?"

"*Ibid.,*" she said. "I'm sure everybody will be very pleased. Except—" She paused.

He knew what she was going to say.

"I told you there might be difficulties. Father thinks there may. Professor Nutter. He doesn't care much for his instructors being too popular. Or so Father says."

Nick had been at first equally startled and gratified at her revelation. Now, however, these reactions were effaced by the forcible recollection of his earlier preoccupations. The several concerns of the morning began to blend in his mind into one large crisis.

"Like Hindmire," he said bleakly.

She looked at him surprised. "Yes, rather. How did you hear about Hindmire?"

In the heat of the moment, he had forgotten both his intention to question her on the subject and the fact that Hindmire's name was never mentioned. A more tactful approach to the subject would have been preferable. But now the case of Hindmire appeared to him in the light of a current emergency, and he proceeded abruptly to the point.

"Nutter was telling me about it this morning. What I want to know is, how did Nutter get on to him?"

Marian, frowning, considered the matter. "I'm surprised Professor Nutter told you about it. It was extremely unpleasant. So unpleasant that it's rarely talked of."

"That's what he told me."

"In some ways it was the most unpleasant thing that's happened here."

"I've gotten the idea that this place kind of specializes in unpleasant things. Like Dr. Winthrop and the stuffed crocodile."

She laughed. "That was quite different," she said, although without specifying how. "What seemed to me most unpleasant about Hindmire's activities was not so much that he lied about his degree—one could understand that, in a way—but that he kept elaborating the lies. He told both Pirbright and the President as well as Clayfoot in great detail about how a lot of important people who'd read his thesis had said it was the best one they'd ever seen. It was all built around some letters of Sarah Orne Jewett's that he'd found, which set forth a new and surprising theory about the art of the short story. And of course he'd never written a thesis at all, let alone found any letters of Sarah Orne Jewett's. After he'd flunked his generals several times, the Harvard people told him to go away and not come back."

These details were of only moderate interest to Nick. He was anxious to ask again what had led Professor Nutter to his fatal exploration of Mr. Hindmire's authenticity. But a degree of discretion now returned to him and prevailed over his impatience. It would not, clearly, be prudent to direct Marian's attention too noticeably toward his concern with this aspect of the affair.

"In a way," she went on, "you couldn't help feeling rather sorry for him. But there was something dirty about it, even after you'd told yourself that he must be suffering from some complicated compulsion. I imagine that he couldn't help himself. But our generation can never quite reconcile old-fashioned beliefs in a moral imperative with new-fashioned beliefs in a psychological imperative. Anyway, the effect of the Hindmire business was to make us all feel *soiled*."

She emphasized her last word heavily. It was clearly the strongest word she could think of, and to Nick's concern for his safety was added the unpleasant sensation that similar revelations about himself would certainly make her feel even more soiled.

"It's made us all rather suspicious," she added. "I think everyone feels that it's not safe to trust anybody."

This offered an opening for him to repeat his original question. "Why didn't Nutter trust him in the first place? What made him decide to investigate Hindmire's doctorate?"

"I suppose simply because he disliked him. Hindmire was very popular. Which brings us back to the *Achaean* elections. It's a great honor, and I hope you're proud of yourself. But Father felt that you ought to be warned of Professor Nutter's reactions."

He was certainly warned. An hour later he was in his office, awaiting with concern the arrival of Mr. Edward Untermeister, editor-in-chief of the *Achaean*, whom he had urgently summoned to his presence. If the election results were merely provisional, as Marian had suggested, it was possible that something could still be done. It was always possible to tamper with election results, and the hope of doing so had led him to call Mr. Untermeister. But he had no plan in mind. And Mr. Untermeister, the D Minus student who had asserted on the first day of English 49 that imagery was the use of images, did not seem a promising man to deal with. It seemed likely that he would not be able to understand what was expected of him even if Nick devised something to expect.

He presently appeared, and his person was in no way reassuring. He looked large, athletic, and unencouraging as he seated himself massively upon a chair. Owing presumably to doubts about his performance in English 49, he also looked apprehensive.

"Yuh wanta see me, sir?" he asked, seeming to anticipate some sinister interrogation. There had been some discussion at the last meeting of English 49 about Hawthorne's use of the Maypole Image to which Mr. Untermeister's contributions had been notably deficient. It was, Nick thought, probable that he expected to be questioned about the Maypole Image.

"Yes, Untermeister." Nick looked at him sternly, but with inward alarm. The boy's face was vacant and bland. He was certainly stupid, but he also looked disquietingly honest. He did not give the impression of a boy who would willingly falsify election results. "I have been hearing rumors," Nick said.

He still had no aim in view, but it would do no harm to increase Mr. Untermeister's apprehensions as part of a softening-up process. And indeed, Mr. Untermeister started at the statement. Like Nick an hour earlier, he looked as if he might have a guilty conscience. Conceivably the air of fatuous honesty was only the product of a dim mind. In the instant that followed, Nick considered the things that Mr. Untermeister might conceivably have a guilty conscience about. It was possible that he had been cheating on examinations, of course. But this gratifying possibility Nick felt it necessary to reject. Not even Mr. Untermeister could have produced so graphic a portrayal of ignorance in his examination if he had received illegal assistance on it. His sin, if any, must be of some more obscure and unhelpful sort. There seemed to be nothing to do except to come to the point.

"About the *Achaean*," he went on, carefully watching Mr. Untermeister's reactions in the hope that they might suggest a policy.

They did not do so. Instead, the boy relaxed. Curiosity, like a faint movement in the current of a muddy stream, illuminated his features.

"Yeah?" he said.

"I hear the results of the elections are known."

"Yeah?" He looked at first a little more curious, and then he seemed to brighten slightly, as if certain implications of Nick's statement had begun to seep into his mind.

"Supposed to be secret. But maybe you heard, sir . . ." He was now positively radiant. It was evident that something in the nature of an idea had come to him, and he undertook the difficult task of translating it into words. "I know," he said slowly, "that I haven't been doing too good in 49. But I sure have enjoyed it. A whole lot. So when we started getting the election results I sure was glad to see—"

"I know. I've heard about the results."

There was a distressing finality about the pause that now ensued. But as Nick rather desperately studied the boy's face, he observed evidence of the appearance of a second idea. The notion that his instructor might be gratified into taking a more lenient attitude in English 49 was apparently being replaced by some more subtle stratagem. It looked as if Mr. Untermeister were conceiving a conspiracy.

"I hope you're pleased, sir," he said at last.

"Oh, yes." Nick acknowledged his success lightly.

"You know, you got some votes for being the most learned professor, too."

Nick's surprise at this unexpected tribute was drowned in his greater surprise at the porcine craft of the editor-in-chief. The impression of naïve honesty was misleading indeed. It seemed more likely that guile, lumbering but Byzantine, was his outstanding trait. Nick's spirits rose. He had, as yet, no plot to match Mr. Untermeister's, but now that the illusion of his honesty was dispelled he felt more confident that some settlement could be arranged.

"I guess you'd like to be voted the most learned professor, wouldn't you?" the student continued. His voice was insinuating, as if he were consciously imitating some archetypal con man from the television screen. "And you know, sir, I got to get another B to graduate. I've been here six years already. I'd sure like to graduate, Dr. Hunter."

Nick regarded him with something approaching affection. This baccalaureate felon, this Little Caesar of academic crime, had miraculously presented him with a ready-made and entirely workable stratagem. He sighed in relief, and with a guile that equalled his fellow-conspirator's he proceeded to the bargaining.

"Did I get any votes for anything else?"

Mr. Untermeister betrayed no surprise at this increase in the price of his B. He seemed indeed to have expected it. His eyes narrowed in a speculative leer. "You got a few votes—not too many—for Most Distinguished. At least I think you did. I don't remember for sure."

"B is a pretty high mark. You'd have trouble getting a B, Untermeister. You haven't been doing so well."

"Yeah." He considered the matter without, however, appearing downcast at this show of sales resistance. "It means a lot to get voted Most Learned and Most Distinguished *both*."

The ease with which the transition had been made to overt trading struck Nick as remarkable. He wondered idly if this sort of thing were common at Parthenon. Mr. Untermeister certainly seemed experienced.

"It might be possible," he said thoughtfully, "for you to get a B. If the right faculty member got voted Most Learned and Most Distinguished. It might be perfectly possible."

"O.K., Dr. Hunter. I guess that might happen."

"But I said the right one, you hear. The one I tell you."

"O.K. I guess maybe you got the most votes after all, Dr. Hunter. I'll check up on that."

"Not me." Nick looked at him austerely. "Somebody else. If somebody else that I tell you got elected Most Learned and Most Distinguished, then you might get a B."

Mr. Untermeister's large mouth opened wide. "Somebody else?"

"Professor Nutter."

"*Professor Nutter?*" Mr. Untermeister was incredulous. "You want Professor Nutter to get Most Learned and Most Distinguished?"

"Right."

"But he didn't get any votes for them. He didn't get any votes for anything."

"O.K. But if he gets elected, you could get a B."

Mr. Untermeister looked at the floor, which he pawed slightly with one foot. "I couldn't do that," he said unexpectedly. "He didn't get any votes at all. I couldn't make the whole thing up, Dr. Hunter. It wouldn't be right." He raised his eyes again. They were shining with a fierce glow of integrity. "It wouldn't be honest."

This nuance in Mr. Untermeister's ethical precepts left Nick stunned. He could only ask, without much conviction, "Not for a B in 49?"

"No, sir. Not for a B."

Revelation came belatedly. "An A, then?"

"I never had an A before."

"Would you like one?"

He reflected. "Yeah," he said somewhat grudgingly, "I guess I would."

"O.K. Done." Nick held out his hand. Mr. Untermeister rose slowly from his chair and grasped it. He still bore an expression of numbed disbelief, but he seemed prepared to accept without further question the ways of learned professors who, operating in spheres beyond his ken, arranged to buy honors for their colleagues. He saluted and slouched out of the office, muttering, "An A in 49."

Left alone, Nick considered the transaction. It had turned out more satisfactorily than he could have hoped. He had eaten his cake—or rather, Stuart Hunter's cake—

and he still had it. Hunter would receive his honors, and in perfect safety. Professor Nutter would be not only appeased but positively pleased by his own glory. Mr. Untermeister would be pleased and so, if he had any, would his parents. It seemed probable that Deans and Registrars would be pleased—it would surely be a relief to them to see the last of Mr. Untermeister. Everyone would be pleased.

Stimulated by this sense of public service, he turned to his mail in a state of satisfaction verging upon smugness. And here a mild shock awaited him in the form of an airmail letter addressed in Stuart Hunter's familiar hand. The revival of their moribund correspondence undid somewhat his pleasant glow of complacency, but he opened the letter without any expectations more disturbing than those of boredom and irritation. But on seeing the contents he stared in surprise. In contrast to Hunter's customary neat writing the letter was a wild scrawl, so nearly illegible that it took some time to decipher it.

Dear Torrente,

Not having heard from you recently, I assume that you have been exposed and gone off somewhere without telling me. I always knew this was bound to happen, but I have to know what happened. If this letter reaches you, you've got to answer at once.

I have been very much upset. I know now that I acted irresponsibly and dishonestly last summer when I let you undertake this insane venture. It was inexcusable of me. I can only justify my behavior by saying I had no experience with the depths of iniquity that you and the Tarragon woman had sunk to.

I left her as soon as I realized the utter depravity of her and her friends, and I am going to return to America as soon as possible. I have been in a very disturbed state and have been obliged to go to a clinic to rest and recover, but as soon as I can get away I shall come to Acropolis. I feel that I have an absolute duty to make a full explanation to the authorities at Parthenon, although I realize that this may cost me my career. If so, it will be no more than I deserve. If not, I shall hope to be reinstated, although that would certainly be more than I deserve after allowing myself to be duped and degraded in this way.

If this reaches you write me immediately at the Clinica Santa Dimpna, Via S. Sepulcro. I'll be here for a little while at least, since I am still very sick from shock.

Very truly yours,
S. Hunter

Nick glazedly regarded the final page of the scrawl, which he still held in his hand, before he laid it down on the table and stared for a time into space. Space offered no solace, nor suggested any suitable course of action, and he began deliberately to sort the rest of the mail. But it contained no solace either; what it contained was another letter from Rome.

He was able to guess at its contents as he opened it. "Darling," it began.

He took a deep breath.

It has all been a stupid mistake—entirely my fault. I am far too impulsive. The boy was a frightful bore, and slightly deranged. I finally ordered him out of the house after he had made a most shocking scene with poor Pio di Biondi, who was such a friend of mine before I met you. Hunter screamed with fury in a most deluded way and kicked the furniture. He said he was going straight to New York to unmask you, but I persuaded him to go instead to a clinic for nervous disorders run by some dear little Irish sisters. He rather fancies being taken care of, but when I inquired yesterday they said he was well enough to leave, and I think he really may go to America. He has some abnormal feeling that he must act as a voice of vengeance or something of that sort. He kept talking about his honor.

It would be far simpler if you came back at once, before he arrives. He has left everything in a terrible state, and no one but you could put my counterfoils in order. Let me know when you will leave for Rome and I shall send the fare.

Diana

This second letter thawed his frozen sensibilities. A deathlike horror was replaced by lively irritation. Lady Tarragon's proprietary attitude outraged him, and her letter he tore into small pieces, which he dropped in the wastebasket.

The sense of outrage at being regarded as Lady Tarragon's possession had, oddly enough, a stimulating effect upon him. Something of the satisfaction that he had experienced after his successful transaction with Mr. Untermeister returned in a rush of determination. It would be equally gratifying, he considered, to display to Lady Tarragon his determination to remain at Parthenon, and his ability to do so. The threat provided by Hunter was certainly more concrete and immediate than the threat of the *Achaean* elections, but so large was his annoyance that he was swept into the conviction that he could somehow contrive a means of dealing with it. The emotions that had engulfed him on the *terrazzo* returned with full force.

In the ensuing half hour of furious concentration, his self-assurance abated somewhat. He was obliged to admit that he could think of no way in which Hunter could be dealt with if he did in fact appear before the authorities of Parthenon. But if his confidence waned, his determination if anything increased. The very difficulties of the situation enhanced, in prospect, the satisfaction that he would feel in demonstrating to Lady Tarragon and Dr. Hunter that Nick Torrente was his own man. Still, there was no denying that at the moment the difficulties did appear insuperable, and he resumed the interrupted activities of the day with no more substantial comfort than a resolute hope that something would occur to him.

Nothing did.

Chapter IX   Compulsory Chapel

The Feast of the Patron of Parthenon, St. Matthias, so carefully planned by President Overton, fell on the day after Nick had received the letters from Stuart Hunter and Lady Tarragon. At twenty minutes past seven in the morning he was in the robing room of the College Chapel. He was alone, staring at a large Gothic cupboard executed in rubbed oak and containing a long row of academic gowns on wire hangers. His mood was at once reflective and somewhat tense, and he stared at the gowns as if he suspected them of harboring a malevolent protoplasm that might at any moment surge forth and envelop him in suffocating yards of black poplin.

This state of mind was occasioned partly by the medieval surroundings, eerily lit by dawn, and the unwonted sight of so many black gowns. It was also the consequence of lack of sleep. He had awakened early, and now had arrived half an hour early to prepare himself for a ceremony that he was not much looking forward to. Illogically, since he had been awake for hours, he resented the schedule that fixed the beginning of the day's activities at 8 A.M. President Overton, he knew, liked chapel services at early hours, on the ground that the college community was more receptive to liturgy when it was half asleep, a taste Nick regarded with disfavor.

He stared thoughtfully at the cupboard and reflected with considerable bitterness upon Stuart Hunter and Lady Tarragon. His determination to confound them had in no way abated since the previous day. The confounding of Lady Tarragon offered no problems. It could be achieved simply through inaction. But he had still thought of no suitable tactic for the confounding of Stuart Hunter. There, positive action was urgently necessary, but his imagination—usually so productive of tactical ideas—had so far failed him. He had taken one measure, but it was merely a delaying operation, and one of whose efficacy he was doubtful. The night before he had gone to Albany (judging that the name of the addressee might give rise to unpleasant curiosity in the local telegraph office) and sent a cable to the Clinica Santa Dimpna. "ALL WELL HERE UNDER NO CIRCUMSTANCES LEAVE ROME UNTIL ARRIVAL VITAL INFORMATION CAN BE TOLD ONLY IN PERSON." After some reflection, he had left it unsigned.

This represented no definitive solution of the Hunter problem. Still, if Hunter's hysteria persisted, the cable might be expected to produce a desirable confusion, since it was open to any number of interpretations, all of them unclear. At worst it should give him a few more days before Hunter, despairing of receiving any vital information, climbed on a plane. But he had not thought of what to do next. His fund of strategy had been exhausted by his transaction with Mr. Untermeister. Indeed, it had occurred to him in a moment of particular bafflement to solicit advice on a commission basis from that master of cunning. Cooler reflection had diverted him from such a course. Blackmail had a nasty sound, especially when practiced against himself.

There was the alternative of flight. If he were to resume his proper identity and start life anew in, say, Flagstaff, Arizona, no problems would be likely to arise. No difficult questions would be asked, at least not of Nick Torrente. But flight, if physically feasible, was still psychologically impossible. More than ever he was determined to beat Stuart Hunter on his own ground. He had to think of something.

He had no doubt that in time he *would* think of something, but it was precisely time that was lacking, and this depressed him. He was unwontedly edgy. The Hindmire affair kept recurring to him. Was there, in fact, some freemasonry of Ph.D.s, some secret formula, ignorance of which was bound sooner or later to be revealed? The thought still troubled him in the midst of his other and more immediate concerns. But mostly he had spent the past day and night preoccupied with vindictive thoughts of Stuart Hunter.

In the course of these unproductive reflections he was joined in the robing room by the first of his colleagues. It was Sid Green, and Nick welcomed him warmly, pleased to have companionship.

"Arrive early to avoid the crush of somnolent scholars," Sid said. "Mitigate the miseries of a mass Mass by robing in tranquility. You look as if you weren't anticipating the ceremonies with much avidity."

"I'm not."

"It will be better next year. It's the marching by juniority that's unsettling. Very painful for the new instructor. Forming the van of a procession brought up by elderly gents of enormous distinction is painful. It puts ideas in one's head. Two years ago, when I led the parade I was troubled by a dangerous fantasy of steering the whole lot of them three times around the ambulatory and then up the belfry. After *his* first year Mike Kelly found the whole responsibility too much for him and abdicated. He hasn't been in a procession since. And Brandon has never been in one."

"How do they get out of it? It says on the notice 'Required of all faculty members.'"

"Well, Brandon was tactfully told by the President that he needn't bother, because of being lame. It would spoil the symmetry. And Mike invoked religious principles. He went to the President with a *crise de conscience* and told him he was being tainted by heresy. Took letters from a priest pointing out the corrosive effects of the Anglican Prayer Book. I considered invoking a rabbi myself, but I hadn't the energy."

"You have scruples? About the Anglican Prayer Book?"

"Well, I could manage a few if necessary. When I was in the Army I used to be converted rather frequently, to take advantage of the religious holidays. Jew for Yom Kippur, Catholic for the Assumption, and, when we were in North Africa, Muslim for Ramadan. You can easily triple your leave that way. But with advancing years a certain scepticism overtakes one." He was sorting his gown and his black-and-orange hood. "Where are your regalia?"

"Here somewhere." Nick began to search in the cupboard. "At least I guess they are. They got me one for Matriculation."

"You should be able to spot the hood easily. There can't be any other doctorates from Oregon. What color is it?"

"Green and something, I think." Nick discovered a green-and-white hood and pulled it out. "This, maybe."

"Good God, man. That's a Dartmouth bachelor's hood. Belongs to the assistant librarian. How about this?" Sid

took out a more voluminous gown faced with blue velvet,
and a hood lined with green-and-yellow silk. "This must
be it. Let me hold it for you."

They helped one another to enrobe themselves and to
adjust the fall of their hoods. Some of the rest of the
faculty had begun to arrive now, noticably unenthusiastic,
and to crowd in front of the cupboard. One of them, an
elderly theologian named Goodge, a scholar of impressive
height and gauntness whom Nick knew only by sight,
paused as if to greet him. He did not do so, however, but
instead circled him slowly, staring fixedly at his back. Such
an unusual interest on the part of a stranger caused Nick
to cower slightly.

"A webfoot," Dr. Goodge remarked in emphatic and
sepulchral tones and passed on.

"Impressive, isn't he?" Sid spoke in a confidential
whisper. "He knows them all. He astounded Shalcross
when he first came by addressing him as a coyote. That's
a very obscure one. Less surprising for me to be called
tiger. Rather unexpected in one of his antiquity and calling,
don't you think?"

The enigmatic nature of Dr. Goodge's lore and of Sid's
commentary diverted Nick to a study of the costume
which had obscurely given rise to it. He had worn it before,
but on none of the previous occasions had anybody addressed him as a webfoot. The attribute of webfootedness
which seemed to attach to the robes suddenly invested
them with a weird and esoteric mystery. He looked down
at himself uneasily.

A distraction, however, now offered itself. A buzzing
half silence began to creep over the faculty, uncomfortably
crowded into the robing room, and then the name of
Stuart Hunter was ringingly announced. The procession
was being formed on the principle of juniority. Nick moved
to the door and took his place at the head of the line beside

his partner in juniority, the new instructor of geology. Behind him, his colleagues, ruggedly resistant to regimentation, combatted the attempts of the marshals to put them in order. After a period of undignified turbulence, the Provost (who bore, as a lesser distinction, the title of Master of Processions) issued a command to march. Nick and the new member of the Department of Geology marched.

In accordance with instructions they marched through the cloister, to whose portly arches a coating of hoarfrost still clung, and thence to the West Portal. Here a pause ensued while the Master of Processions redressed disparities in the table of precedence and attempted to discipline his charges into a more seemly bearing. The atmosphere was for some minutes that of the Queen of Hearts' croquet ground on a very cold day, but at length they moved forward to enter, with majestic pace, the Portal.

It was a long procession, for on the Feast of the Patron the Board of Trustees was invited to participate and a number of them had gone so far as to do so. By the time Nick and the geology instructor had traversed the length of the nave and taken their places in the choir stalls, the most senior of the faculty were still passing under the portal and the trustees and President were still shivering outside. The organ, loud, lugubrious, and majestic, drowned the effort of the congregation to make audible the words of a hymn. The effect was unquestionably impressive.

So too, unexpectedly, were the setting and the procession. The chapel was very large and almost dark, with only the winter dawn sending thin rays through the stained glass. The high vaults, their architectural naïvetés lost in shadow, reverberated. And down the aisle came the slow parade with its mystic coloring of webfoot, coyote, and tiger. The President undoubtedly knew what he was doing. The atmosphere was both stately and stirring.

As the procession ended, the President in a golden cope, attended by a suite only slightly less gorgeously attired, took his place before the spotlit altar with its grove of candles. The censers, rhythmically swinging, flooded the chapel with evocative clouds of frankincense. The dazzling figure of Dr. Overton knelt, and the congregation in turn fell silently to its knees. For a time silence pervaded the towering spaces of the chapel.

In this dim and potent silence Nick found himself perspiring. The effects of extreme trepidation, clinging from Hunter's letter, and of elusive unease, clinging from Dr. Goodge's cryptic lore, burgeoned with remarkable speed and luxuriance. He was in a very sensitive state indeed. His psychic tension mounted; the silence continued.

It was broken abruptly by the President's thunderous voice, rolling out into the vaulted spaces, incantatory and echoing, with the arresting effect of a sudden peal of bells. The effect on Nick of the words thus powerfully intoned was not only arresting but alarming.

Almighty God, unto whom all hearts are open and all desires known, and from whom no secrets are hid. . . .

He recoiled physically, as though the remarkable resonance of the President's voice had through some sonic mischance produced a sharp pain in his ears. But the effect of this minatory message certainly was the consequence of some Force of greater magnitude than even the President's voice. Nick felt impulsively that it would be safer to leave the chapel, and with haste.

He pulled himself together, and cautiously sought to close his ears to these unsettlingly apposite passages. Both the President's volume and the mesmeric words hindered the effort. He presently succeeded in diverting his mind to other channels, but the sense of a reproachful Presence persisted.

The service was positively alive with relevances. "Ye,"

he was instructed, "who do truly and earnestly repent you of your sins, and are in love and charity with your neighbors, and intend to lead a new life, following the commandments of God . . ." He shuddered. In several senses, certainly he was obeying the injunction to lead a new life, but none of these senses could be construed as appropriate.

". . . and are heartily sorry for these our misdoings; the remembrance of them is grievous unto us; the burden of them is intolerable. Have mercy upon us. . . ."

He shuddered again.

The Mass rolled on impressively to its conclusion, and Nick approached the Recessional in a painful condition of detachment from the physical realities around him. He had been exhorted to repent and to repair his ways. Repentance he was prepared, in his now shaken state, to undertake. Repair was more difficult. But as the Procession neared the Portal on its return journey, there came to him something in the nature of a revelation, or, more exactly, a sudden reshuffling of his attitudes. He had just been enjoined to love his neighbor as himself. Having spent the last few hours and indeed the last few months in hating Stuart Hunter, there now came to him a sudden realization that his determination to frustrate that irritating scholar no longer arose strictly from a vindictive spirit. In a quite unprecedented spirit of self-examination, he abruptly concluded that his wish to remain at Parthenon College no longer had much to do with Stuart Hunter. It arose, he was astonished to discover, from a positive liking for the place. His wish to dispose of Hunter was involved, too, with a certain odd feeling of responsibility toward Parthenon. He very much disliked the thought that the destinies of his students might be confided to the authentic Hunter. For if the one were fraudulent—or, better, fictitious —the other was evidently demented. A sense of duty demanded every possible effort to prevent his replacement by a demented if genuine instructor of English.

And as these considerations chased one another rapidly across his mind a further and more practical revelation came to him. A policy for disposing of Hunter presented itself, suddenly and without evident cause. Two trains of thought, one running along lines of patron saints, and the other charged with thoughts of Hunter's dementedness and the dear little Irish Sisters, collided in an illuminating flash. Santa Dimpna, some obscure hagiological recollection from his days in Rome informed him, was the patroness of the mentally ill. In an instant, a plan had formed itself in his mind.

His mental processes, having been afloat in an incensed trance, at once became businesslike and incisive. A cablegram must be sent—again—and from some moderately remote telegraph office where locally familiar names would create no curiosity. Casual encounters would have to be arranged with both the President and Professor Nutter and a message inserted into conversation with them. All of this was urgent, and it would not be easy. His classes must be met. Then he would be obliged to absent himself from Convocation in the afternoon, to reach Albany or some other suitable point. A car would have to be borrowed. Suitable occasions for insinuating conversations would have to be arranged. And everything would have to be done as soon as possible.

For the moment, action was impossible. Custom required the academic procession to halt outside the chapel and wait for the congregation to come out. It took some time. The morning was very cold, and the faculty drew its robes tightly and shivered. Nick was less affected by cold than by impatience, but there was still one more ritual; the faculty and congregation sang the *Alma Mater*.

The crowd was large, the tempo very slow, the noise stupendous. It echoed in the icy air from the chapel to the walls of an adjacent dormitory like a series of cannon shots. Nick had been through this before without experiencing any emotion but mild embarrassment. In his present mood he found the effect imposing. The tune seemed to him both stirring and original—had he been more familiar with hymns he would have recognized the air of *Fling Out the Banner*—and even the words of the first stanza seemed temporarily fraught with meaning.

> *Above the flow of Mohawk's stream*
> *Thy bright lamp throws a goodly beam.*
> *Its light, our sun, will guide us on*
> *Beneath the elms of Parthenon.*

The second stanza, sung in a nostalgic murmur, was more moving still, but its message was from Nick's point of view less fortunate.

> *But youth is brief and fades away,*
> *And only memories live. Today*
> *We bask upon thy hearth. Anon*
> *We'll leave the elms of Parthenon.*

And the final stanza, although shouted in a triumphant roar and at faster tempo, did not console him much.

> *But yet above fair Mohawk's strand*
> *Thy stately temples still will stand,*
> *Though memories dim and we be gone*
> *From 'neath the elms of Parthenon.*

The urgency of his task was emphasized by these lugubrious sentiments. Happily he remarked Professor Nutter detaching himself from the crowd and managed to reach his side as he started across the campus toward Xenophon.

"Anachronistic," Professor Nutter said. He seemed to refer to the service, perhaps to religious observances in general. "A blight."

"You think it's a blight, sir?" Even for one who thought religious observances anachronistic it seemed an extreme judgment.

"The elm blight. It killed them all. But of course they couldn't say ''neath the maples.'"

"I can see that." Nick was thoughtful. "It wouldn't fit in."

"They could say oaks, but there aren't any. No better than elms. No firs, either."

Nick looked around him. The campus seemed to be heavily wooded despite the demise of the elms, but his botanical knowledge did not extend to knowing if there were any one-syllable trees in sight.

"Indecent," Professor Nutter said, although whether in reference to the elm blight, the *Alma Mater,* or perhaps again the chapel service, was unclear.

"Yes, sir," Nick agreed automatically.

"Prostitution." Professor Nutter laughed gaily.

"Prostitution?"

"Exactly. You saw them talking?"

"Ah—" Nick considered. "Who?"

"Babcock and the President. They were working it out together, by the Portal. I overheard them. He is coming next week."

Nick had a moment of irrational alarm. "Who?" he asked.

"A Swiss sociologist. Purview told me. Babcock is giving him as a present. Two lectures, Purview says. He will be in residence for several weeks. Woodbine is probably behind it. Nobody else will be."

"No," said Nick. And he sighed deeply.

"Purview says that he is not just a sociologist. He is hyphenated. Psycho. Or anthropo. Or culturo." Professor Nutter chuckled. "In any case, pseudo."

Nick sighed again.

This time Professor Nutter took notice. "Asthma?" he asked. "Nasty thing. Old Carstairs had to give up teaching because of his asthma."

"Not asthma," Nick said hastily. "I've had bad news."

"Glad to hear it, Stuart," Professor Nutter said kindly, his anxiety about asthma allayed. "And speaking of giving up teaching, there's something important I want to talk to you about. I got the enrollment reports for the second semester from the Registrar yesterday. They're always late. Too much pay, too little work. You should have told me." He shook his finger in a gesture of mischievous satisfaction.

"Told you what, sir?"

"I had no idea you had so many more people enrolled for your courses this semester. Sixty-four in English 49. Quite a change from Clayfoot's day. It's absolutely ruined Semantics 31, which meets at the same hour. I fear we may expect reprisals from Woodbine." Professor Nutter laughed aloud.

Nick sighed once more. There was no time to waste.

"If only," Professor Nutter went on with the utmost cordiality, "Clayfoot had had the sense to appoint men like you. . . ."

The sighs having failed, Nick gave a low groan.

Still Professor Nutter proceeded cheerfully. "It confirms all my hopes. I have written to the President. We don't speak, you know. I have recommended your reappointment for next year."

This was sufficiently striking for Nick temporarily to forget his plan. "Is that right?" he asked with pleasure.

"I hope you will continue to bring credit on the Department. Of course, the President will oppose it. He always opposes anything I recommend. But in the end he will have to give in."

"I am pleased, Professor Nutter," Nick said quickly. "Very pleased. And grateful. I need good news right now. I have just had some very bad news."

"Too bad. Now, as regards Shalcross, I have asked the President to make a terminal appointment. What do you think of that?"

"Very bad news indeed," Nick repeated.

"I do not," Professor Nutter went on, "approve of gossiping within the Department. But I don't mind telling you that young man is not satisfactory."

"Very bad news indeed," said Nick desperately.

"You don't approve of letting Shalcross go?" Professor Nutter was surprised.

"I didn't mean that, sir. I have just had some very bad news."

Professor Nutter apparently heard this for the first time. "Your mother?" he asked in concern. "Or your father?"

Nick sighed, this time out of sheer relief. "My first cousin."

"Ah." Professor Nutter seemed uninterested in first cousins.

"A young man," Nick spoke convulsively, "just my age."

"An automobile accident, I suppose. Now, as regards the position of Pelz . . ."

For the first time in their association, Nick interrupted him. "Worse," he said violently. "He's gone crazy."

"Gone crazy?" Professor Nutter's attention returned to the subject.

"He's mad." Nick sought to drive the point home. "Disturbed."

"What disturbed him?"

"He is in Rome. . . ."

"It doesn't disturb most people. But I did have an old aunt in Minneapolis who thought the Pope was going to come there to Get Her. We finally had to put her away."

"We think we may have to put *Cousin Stuart* away too." Nick emphasized the name. "He's imagining things. Like your aunt."

"About the Pope?"

"No, about me. That is to say, he imagines he *is* me, and . . ."

"Odd. Very odd. Still, these things happen. Perhaps a good rest. Now, regarding Pelz, I was about to say . . ."

Nick could do no more. At least he had forced the basic data upon Professor Nutter's attention. If the matter of a second Stuart Hunter ever came up, Nick suspected Professor Nutter would remember the conversation. For all his rambling manner he had a singularly tenacious memory.

The President was going to be harder to get at. He was not accessible; the promised bowling contests had never materialized. And it was clearly impossible to make an appointment with him for the sole purpose of discussing Cousin Stuart's sanity. On the other hand the President would be at the Reception for the Trustees that afternoon. An opportunity would have to be found then.

In the meantime there was the cable. After some thought Nick asked Mike Kelly to lend him his car.

"Sure," said Mike, "or, better yet I'll take you wherever you want to go. I want to get out of this trap for a while."

Nick was disconcerted. Now he would have to invent an excuse for the trip. But, as it turned out, Mike was too preoccupied with his own concerns to have any interest in Nick's. His first words as he slid behind the wheel and started the motor were, "The damned bastards," spoken in nameless hatred. His face beneath his turbulent red hair was preternaturally white.

"Who?" Nick asked.

"Pretty much everybody," Mike said. "At the moment, the Parthenon faculty."

"What's the matter?"

"Everything."

Nick, doubting whether Mike really wanted to say more, was silent.

"They may talk about Wittgenstein," Mike said suddenly after some miles, "but that doesn't stop them from meddling all the time. For the pure joy of it. Like any other small-town gossips. They act as if they have to act more like everybody else than everybody else. In order to conceal the social solecism of being learned, I suppose."

There was another silence. "They talk," Mike went on after a time, looking whiter than ever, "they talk all the time. If you're a good teacher and a good scholar you ought to be allowed to have some private life of your own without people talking. That Nutter woman of yours is the worst."

"What's she been doing now?"

"Talking." Mike, stopping for a light, applied his foot to the brake with a gesture like a kick. The car bucked. "To me, as well as to everybody else. She *warned* me."

"What of?"

"Trouble," said Mike bleakly, and with this he fell into a silence that lasted until Albany.

Trouble was certainly in the air. Nick was genuinely concerned with Mike's, but once they arrived in Albany his full attention was given to his own. Briskly he provided himself with five dollars in change, found a public telephone, and dictated the message he had composed that morning between classes. He had put a good deal of thought into it.

STUART HUNTER CLINICA SANTA DIMPNA ROME ITALY
SITUATION ENGLISH FULLY CLARIFIED COMPLETE SATIS-
FACTION SOLUTION PERMANENT BASIS OWING URGENCY
POSITION FILLED NO FURTHER OPENING POSSIBLE REGRETS
CORDIALLY OVERTON

He gave his name as Edward P. Overton, of 17 Hudson
Street, Watervliet.

Telegrams, he reflected, were an extraordinarily satisfactory way of communicating with Stuart Hunter. The
tradition of omitted connectives and no punctuation permitted a confusion exactly suited to his needs. This advantage he felt he had fully exploited. Today's cable was
gratifyingly devoid of meaning, but it conveyed an unmistakable indication of finality enveloped in good feeling.
It was a satisfactory offensive blow. And if by any chance
it failed he was already constructing a defense. He scarcely
noticed Mike's silences on the way home. He was too busy
mapping out his strategy for the Reception.

As he arrived, Mrs. Overton, tossing her blond curls,
greeted him graciously and with an extra squeeze of her
hostessly hand. But, he was depressed to see, her husband
had already deserted the receiving line to mingle with his
guests. He abandoned Mrs. Overton as quickly as possible
and went in search of him.

He found him surrounded by a cluster of trustees, drinking some species of fruit juice. Nick considered the situation. It was going to be difficult to detach Dr. Overton
from the encircling trustees, and he could not very well
discuss his cousin in front of them. But a growing sense of
urgency impelled him forward. The cable might at this
very minute rest in the quavering hands of Stuart Hunter,
and if Hunter were moved—the possibility had only recently occurred to him—to the transatlantic telephone, a
fatal bell might ring at any moment. Contemplating the

thick cordon of trustees, he wondered if a night letter would have been wiser.

But as he watched, a sudden tidal change in the social sea took place. A number of trustees floated toward the punch bowl. The waters drew back, leaving a dry path to the President. Nick advanced toward him.

"Good afternoon, sir. A very pleasant occasion." He assumed a voice of distracted anxiety.

"Hunter. Good. Glad you're here. It's important for you young men to meet the trustees. Important for them to meet you, too. Show them we're not all ready for the grave at Parthenon."

"Yes, sir," Nick said sadly.

The President was by temperament and profession a good deal more sensitive than Professor Nutter to the intonations of those about him. He eyed Nick searchingly. "You seem melancholy, Hunter. Bad thing, melancholy. What we need is vigor and good spirits, particularly on the Feast of the Patron."

"I've had some very bad news."

The President's manner changed at once. The jovial host was replaced by the understanding confessor. He assumed the appearance of a paternal polar bear. A sort of island of solace erupted, through the force of his personality, above the moiling sea of social amenities.

"My dear boy, can I be of help?"

"Well, sir." Nick shuffled his feet with a hesitancy not altogether assumed and felt the President's powerful hand drop on his shoulder. "A family matter. I've had bad news about a cousin."

He wondered suddenly if a cousin was sufficiently convincing; his voice shook conveniently. "A *first* cousin. Just my age. And the same name. We have been very close." He enunciated these data carefully. It was important that they be clearly understood. "But I oughtn't to bother you with these personal things."

The President waved this away. "If I can be of any help, either as priest or president, I am at your disposal."

"He has gone—that is, he has become seriously disturbed. A breakdown. I have had word from Rome that he has had a serious breakdown. But I'm afraid there's not much anyone can do."

"These things," the President said benevolently but with a shade less concern, "are very distressing. But with the resources of modern—"

"He has delusions," Nick said hurriedly. He realized that the President's interest in his problem was lessened by the news that the problem was in Rome and so unable to profit from the President's personal attention. But there were vital points still to be made. "Terrible delusions. Very upsetting. Especially for me."

"I quite understand. . . ."

"We have always been very close. We were brought up together, you know, and now . . ."

"Perhaps you would find it less distressing not to dwell on these details," the President said kindly, looking toward the punch bowl.

"And now he has developed a confusion of identities." Nick produced this technical phrase with some satisfaction. "He has confused himself with me. He imagines that our identities are reversed, they tell me." Dr. Overton turned back to him with some eagerness.

"Reversal of identity, you say? The Schneck-Uberhoff Trauma, do you suppose?"

"Maybe," Nick said. "I haven't any details."

"Most interesting. I have myself only just been hearing about the Schneck-Uberhoff Trauma." The President paused. "I *believe* that identity was involved. It was Mr. Babcock who was discussing the matter. He knows

Schneck-Uberhoff personally. He has been visiting in Switzerland. You would find it helpful to talk to Mr. Babcock."

It was obviously a dismissal, and Nick accepted it. His purpose was accomplished. He permitted himself to be propelled in the general direction indicated by Dr. Overton, and settled down to enjoy the fruit juice.

The following morning he confronted English 49 with self-confidence fully restored. The yearbook was taken care of. Hunter was taken care of. In the next hour Mark Twain would be taken care of. He had worked out, the night before, a brief introductory lecture on the themes the class should bear in mind in considering the works of this author, a brief résumé of certain dominant leitmotifs and some pertinent remarks on the relation of the artist to the cultural background of his era.

He entered the classroom a little late and took his place on the platform with the nonchalant air he had been perfecting over the months. It was his habit now to omit the reading of the rollbook or even any scrutiny of the students assembled before him. Rather he would gaze offhandedly out of the window, or at some distant point on the ceiling, and begin to speak without preliminaries. Later, having completed his lecture, he would engage in urbane but erudite dialogue with the students.

"Today," he said, "we approach Mark Twain!"

He noted with satisfaction that he had succeeded in conveying a suggestion of solemn finality, as if they were approaching a long-sought destination. This ought to make them think, if anything could, that Mark Twain was worth approaching.

"Before we begin discussing the books, there are some points I would like to draw your attention to. They are all very obvious things which you will probably have noticed for yourselves"—he had found this a suitable formula for

inculcating a despairing sense of unworthiness in the audience—"but perhaps they're worth putting in some kind of
order. Besides noting such obvious matters as the persist-
ence of the River Image and the Navigation Symbolism,
I want to say a few words about the significance of race
relations, the firearm themes, and the feud motifs in the
early writings. I'll also have a word or two to say about
the counter-frontier conflict, the god-devil identification
with ancient cultures, particularly in *A Connecticut Yankee*
and *A Tramp Abroad*, and in general the whole question
of *Europäischtum*."

"Sir . . ." Several members of the class had raised their
hands, as he had intended they should. He prepared to
write *Europäischtum* on the blackboard and to explain,
concisely and with a hint of condescension, its meaning.
He turned to look at the class for the first time and to
recognize a student who would question him about this
technicality. As he did so he saw that there was a visitor.
In the back of the room, on one of the chairs normally
unoccupied, a stranger was sitting. Mildly interested, even
flattered, by this unusual attention, Nick glanced at the
visitor as he nodded to one of the members of the class
who had raised his hand.

As he did so he became aware with incredulous horror
that the visitor was a stranger only in the restricted sense
of being alien. His head was raised, and he was staring
fixedly at Nick. His expression, too, was indicative of incredulity and of a certain wide-eyed wildness, but his
features were stunningly familiar.

The cost of Nick's cables had been wasted.

Stuart Hunter had arrived in Acropolis.

Chapter X   *Expulsion and Suspension*

Nick was accustomed to unexpected crises. The terms of his life had been chronically critical, and he was trained to confront them. He reacted to Stuart Hunter with a sense of shock, certainly, but with an instant appraisal of requirements and possibilities.

Their eyes had met briefly, and in that instant Nick made certain rapid observations. Hunter was tired, unhappy, and tense, but he was not, judging from his expression, absolutely deranged. His behavior was going to be eccentric, but it was not likely to be violent. He was, Nick thought, calculable. And there was something else he thought he observed; the most striking feature of Hunter's gaze when their eyes met was one of shock, of shock even greater than his own. For this state there could be only one explanation—Hunter was surprised to find that Nick was still here, and much more surprised to discover him competently referring to things like *Europäischtum* before an audience studiously and respectfully taking notes. The brief display of competence he had witnessed had undoubtedly upset Stuart Hunter a good deal.

This shock was a precious if temporary asset. It might not help in the larger problem raised by Hunter's presence, but it should enable Nick to get through the present hour without catastrophe. For the moment his aim must be to keep Hunter quietly in his place at the back of the room and if possible to increase his confusion. Obviously this would require the greatest possible display of academic virtuosity. *Europäischtum* and Navigation Symbolism had served to stun the intruder. It would take further literary blows to induce concussion. It was going to have, in short, to be good.

All these considerations passed through Nick's mind as he wrote *Europäischtum* on the blackboard, which fortunately involved turning his back on the class. He also wrote down Feud Motif and Culture Conflict, quite unnecessarily, and by the time he had turned to face the class again he had recovered his air of competence. Averting his eyes from the calamitous figure at the back of the room, he undertook to dazzle.

"As an example of the use of these themes," Nick said, "I want to talk first very briefly about *Huckleberry Finn*." This was an impromptu and perhaps perilous departure from his previous plans. The class had not yet begun to read *Huckleberry Finn*, and he had not prepared himself to discuss it. But he knew that *Huckleberry Finn* was a good deal more likely to impress Hunter—who couldn't know that the class wouldn't have any idea what Nick was talking about—than anything else. It would also be a good deal easier to display virtuosity with *Huckleberry Finn* than *Life on the Mississippi*.

"Here we've got more clearly than anywhere else most of the themes I have mentioned—worked into a work of art.

TWO

It's artistic even though it's written in the form of artless folklore, and even though the author at the beginning denies having any moral or aesthetic intention."

He had been reading something along these lines in the past few days, and he thought with satisfaction that it sounded extremely good.

"First, let's take race relations and the River Image. Here you could say Mark Twain has used slavery, which was what people were worrying most about in the days he was writing about—as a symbol. What's it a symbol of? Well, of the human condition as a whole. He has *related*"—this word he emphasized heavily, aware that it was a word of peculiar popularity among contemporary thinkers and likely to impress Hunter—"the Negro slave to the white boys; together you can take them as the raw material of human psychology, and he *related* both to the flow of the Mississippi toward the sea. You've got to look at the book as a story of the search for freedom through *relating* among human beings."

A hand went up. Nick nodded.

"Do you mean, sir, that the river is a freedom symbol?"

"Conceptually, no." Nick felt some satisfaction in this reply. It had, he thought, no meaning, but it suggested a rich and measured complexity of ideas. "You can say the river is the symbol of a path *toward* freedom, purification, and stuff—Water Imagery, you understand—but not of freedom itself."

"Thank you, sir."

Nick went on. Over the past few months he had noticed that the period of an hour which had been endless in September had gradually grown shorter and shorter, until now he resented the bell when it finally rang and cut short his expositions. And not even Hunter's presence turned this hour into an ordeal. So great was his concentration on Mark Twain and the symbolism of rivers, so intent was he on the need for virtuosity, that the hour passed even faster than usual. Words like "shamanistic" flowed easily from his lips. With an ironic sense of its singular appropriateness to one listener, he dwelt on metamorphic identity transfers. He was still talking about Imagination Commitments when the bell rang.

He was on the whole satisfied. The students, to be sure, seemed startled by his flow of oratory, uninterrupted by the usual dialogue, about a novel they had not read, but he was satisfied that the softening up of Stuart Hunter had been advanced by it.

The class dispersed, some of its members glancing with casual curiosity at the visitor as they left. The visitor himself was still sitting motionless, sunk in his chair. Nick hoped that this limp and immobile condition was the consequence of shock, but whatever its cause, it was certainly convenient. It would not have done to have Hunter mixing with the departing students.

He waited on the platform until the last of them had departed. Then he moved sternly and majestically toward the back of the room. As he approached Hunter, an opening speech, familiar and reliable, took shape involuntarily.

"Why," he asked austerely, "are you here?"

Hunter looked at him unhappily. "I came," he said sadly, "to talk to Dean Scarlett."

"Oh, you did, did you?" Nick's voice did not change but he had an inward sense of panic. This was one thing he hadn't thought of—the most obvious and serious weakness in his defenses. With the President or Professor Nutter there would have been at least a chance of withstanding the siege. With Dean Scarlett and his link with Dr. Campion there could be none. There was no possible countermove. Nick resorted to evasionary tactics.

"I guess our bet's off," he said, "but if it isn't, I've won.

They told me yesterday I'm going to be reappointed for next year."

There was not much change of expression on Hunter's face, and what there was conveyed not so much astonishment as despair. "There is," Stuart Hunter said, "nothing left. Everything is gone."

So deep was his air of despairing gloom that Nick felt a momentary sense of despair himself. The empty, dreary classroom with its stale air and gaunt furnishings provided an apt setting for the infinite loneliness of mankind. Nick thought of Mark Twain and pulled himself together. If Hunter had talked himself into a state of suicidal depression, so much the better.

"Get hold of yourself, Hunter," he said briskly.

"Everything is a fake. Everything is meretricious. There is no truth anywhere. Everything is fraud and imposture."

To this desolate statement Nick reacted with considerable annoyance. It was, he realized, not his intellectual attainments that had made Hunter despair, but rather the contemptible ease with which he had demonstrated that intellectual attainments could be counterfeited. His reappointment, his command of river symbolism and metamorphic identity transfers, had thrown Hunter into a state not of simple shock but of moral hopelessness. After the revelation of the infinite iniquity of Rome, Nick's perversion of critical jargon, and the evidence of infinite gullibility at Parthenon, had destroyed the last of Stuart Hunter's morale.

"What," he asked, "will become of me?"

"I don't know."

"There is nothing left."

"Maybe you ought to—" Nick broke off. Even if Hunter were willing to listen to him, it was very difficult to think what in fact should be done with him. It would be very undesirable indeed for him to return to Oregon. And—

"I'd rather die than go back to Rome."

"No. You better not do that. Do you have any family?"

"I can never face them. . . ."

"Where are they?"

"In Colorado."

Colorado seemed ideal. "A good rest in Colorado, and you'll feel better. You can explain that you've had a—disturbed period." Nick felt once again master of the situation, although an uneasy master.

Hunter nodded. It looked almost as if he were considering the Colorado project. It seemed to Nick too good to be true that his difficulties should evaporate so rapidly. He was right; it was.

"Before I do anything else," Hunter said, "I must see Dean Scarlett. I have to explain everything."

"Why?"

"Even if you promised to go away," Hunter said, "I couldn't trust you to keep your promise."

"Hell," Nick said.

There was a moment's silence during which Hunter sat staring glazedly, evidently unable to summon the energy or courage to find Dean Scarlett, and Nick regarded him with dislike. And in the course of contemplating all the many features of the situation that contributed to this dislike he struck on one which seemed, especially at the moment, particularly provoking. "Why the hell didn't you ever mention this Campion character to me?" he asked. And then, his mind going further above these lines, he added, "And what the hell did you do to poor Clarissa?"

The effect of the last question was dramatic. Hunter sprang up and eyed Nick with hatred. "Cad," he said.

"Who, me? *I* haven't done anything to Clarissa. It seems to me it was a hell of a way to treat the poor girl. Even if she was a little overweight." As he spoke he realized that the knowledge these words must seem to contain was placing him in a position of strong advantage. "Giving her all that stuff about salmon swimming upstream, and then dropping her cold." His voice, by a supreme effort of dramatic inflection was genially reproachful. He spoke as one roué to another.

Hunter now registered a combination of horror and fury. He clutched Nick's arm roughly as if to get a grip on him before he swung at his jaw.

This was one form of aggression from which Nick had nothing to fear. "The Scarletts are pretty upset about what you did to Clarissa," he said. "You seem to be kind of rough the way you handle women. Diana's pretty upset, too, you know. Kicking the furniture, and insulting poor old Pio di Biondi."

"You bastard," Hunter said. "You scheming, illiterate bastard. You *dastard!*"

Nick laughed. "Bastard or dastard, whatever you want. But if I were you I wouldn't go see Dean Scarlett. I don't think you'd get a very warm welcome. Not after Clarissa."

"How does he know?" Hunter, regaining some control of himself, dropped his hold on Nick's sleeve. "How do *you* know? If *he* knows, why are you still here?"

Nick ignored the questions. "I think the best thing for you to do is go and have a good rest in Colorado."

It became clear as he said it that this was a tactical error. "I came here all the way from Rome to face this thing and to tell them what you are." Hunter was speaking with a visible effort at reasonableness now, his blue eyes pallidly intense. "And I'm going to do it before I go. You've already ruined my life. I'm not going to let you ruin everybody else's. I've nothing left but my honor, and I am damn well going to vindicate that. That's why I came here first, before I went to see Scarlett. It was the only honorable thing to do."

"Diana was right about one thing, anyway," Nick said

musingly. "You sure are on an honor kick. How do you make out that I ruined *your* life? It looks to me more like you'd ruined mine. And you're trying to do it again."

"You conspired with Diana," Hunter said.

"Why would I?"

Before Hunter could answer this question, which seemed to Nick unanswerable, their attention was diverted by the sound of a door opening behind them. Nick looked reflexively at his watch. There would be another class in this room during the following hour, and it was possible that some early-comers were already arriving. He turned around hastily. Professor Nutter had started to move toward the platform carrying his briefcase before he noticed them.

"Ah, my boy," he said, addressing Nick.

"Good morning, sir."

Professor Nutter altered his course and approached them. Nick put one hand on the back of a chair to steady himself and graciously performed the necessary introduction.

"This," he said, his voice almost even, "is Professor Nutter, the Acting Chairman of the English Department. *This is Stuart Hunter, of whom you have heard, sir.*" He spoke the last sentence with an intensity that he hoped would serve his needs equally well with both parties.

Hunter appeared dazed. He had not, apparently, expected an occasion for the vindication of his honor to present itself so promptly. Professor Nutter on the other hand looked for an instant completely puzzled. "*Stuart Hunter?*" he said.

There was a moment's silence.

"Oh," he went on. "Stuart *Hunter*." His face cleared. "Of course, Stuart Hunter. Too bad," he said in sad but polite tones to Stuart Hunter, "too bad. I understand you have been unwell."

Nick sighed, though not audibly, with relief. Hunter tottered backward. At the moment he looked as unwell as it was possible for anyone to look.

"Well," Professor Nutter went on rather quickly, "if you'll excuse me, I want to run over my notes on Nostradamus and Ignatius Loyola before class." It was clear that he was anxious to disengage himself from the lunatic cousin, whom he regarded warily with a sidelong glance. "I am sure I leave you in good hands," he said, nodding to Hunter as he started to turn back to the platform. "You must take care of yourself, young man. A good rest"—he had already started to move away from them—"often does wonders."

"I have been suggesting Colorado," Nick said to his retreating figure. "A good rest in Colorado. The air."

"Excellent," Professor Nutter said over his shoulder. "An excellent notion. Nothing could be better."

"But listen—" Hunter leapt forward convulsively. "You've got to listen."

Professor Nutter's pace quickened. "Colorado," he said, "would be just the thing. Or perhaps Alaska. The air, I am told, in Alaska is excellent." He had reached the platform. "And now, if you will excuse me . . ."

Nick took Hunter by the arm. He was limp again, and he made no resistance as he was forcibly propelled to the door. As they reached it Nick turned to Professor Nutter and their eyes met. Nick smiled, wanly.

"Distressing," Professor Nutter said more cheerfully as they left the room. "Most distressing."

The defenses had withstood the siege.

Once outside Nick steered his now completely unresisting charge toward Theseion Street. He must be got out of sight as soon as possible, but humanitarian motives were also playing their part in the action. Nick had become genuinely concerned about Hunter, who appeared to be threatened with the sort of malady that overtakes a punctured inner tube. Triumphant, Nick had lost his animus against the vanquished and was already thinking about what could be done to salvage Hunter's future without endangering his own. But, first, prudence required consolidation of the victory.

"You see?" he said.

"No." Hunter spoke with a sort of crushed tenacity. He had weakened, but he had not quite given up. Nick had forgotten his talent for stubbornness.

"You will if you think about it," he said carelessly. "Look, friend, you don't stand a chance around here. If you try anything else, you're just going to get yourself in trouble. I'm not just talking, Hunter. It's a fact. Believe me, as regards Acropolis, New York, you've had it."

"I don't understand what's happened," Hunter said with plaintive doggedness.

"Maybe not. It's pretty complicated. But it won't do you any good to stick around here the way things are. You would only find yourself in very embarrassing situations."

Hunter turned to stare at him with a kind of anguished shrewdness. "I think," he said slowly and hopelessly, "that you must be the Devil."

"No." Nick was cheerful. "Not the Devil. Just a marble faun. And I'd say you've got only yourself to blame. In fact you said that in your letter."

"Oh, God." It was evident that Hunter was accessible to this reasoning. "Oh, God, what have I done?"

"That's better." Nick paused and then added, "I'm taking you to my place. You'll feel better when you've had a drink and a hot bath."

The prescription was made more for form's sake than from any confidence in its efficacy, but Nick wanted a chance to think, to prepare some program for the definitive liquidation of the Stuart Hunter menace and some provision for the menace's future. Both prudence and charity required that he not be left hanging as a loose end. But it was true that when he emerged from the bath, holding a half-empty glass, Hunter looked somewhat better.

Nick was businesslike. "Now," he said, "you better sit down and listen for a while. I can see this has all been very tough, Hunter, and the best thing to do is to forget everything that's happened since last August."

"You think I could forget it? Everything is gone," Hunter reverted dismally to his earlier theme. "My career, my principles, my honor," he repeated, but in somewhat calmer tones than he had used before. It sounded as if he were getting used to the idea of these extensive losses.

"You must make a new start," Nick said. "Now let's look at the possibilities. You can't go back to Rome—at least I guess you don't want to. You can't go to Oregon—not after the trouble with Clarissa. And you certainly can't stay here. Too much is known." He broke off. He had been going to suggest Colorado again, but he stopped himself. Colorado was not, it seemed, a good idea. "Is there anything else you really *want* to do?"

Hunter swallowed and looked pensive. "I don't know. If only I knew what had happened . . ."

It was precisely such paths as this that Nick did not want Hunter's mind to traverse. "Now look," he said quickly, "don't you want to write a book or something? Maybe you could make a reputation writing a book, and get a job on the strength of it."

Hunter said nothing, but sipped his drink.

"Have you finished that Hawthorne book?"

"No. I was going to work on it last autumn, but . . ."

"Would you like to work on it now? If it's any good, you might even make some money." He was doubtful about this, but it was not altogether impossible. "It would make you feel better if you finished it, anyway. You could go to someplace where they have a good library and live quietly. Nobody would know who you were. You could make new friends and finish the book."

"I don't have any money."

"I think that could be fixed up, maybe. For a while. I've got some saved up. You don't have much chance to spend money in Acropolis. I'd be glad to give you a kind of fellowship. For a year, say. Would two thousand bucks help any? I can spare that. To further the cause of Hawthorne scholarship."

"I couldn't take your money," Hunter said, with a slight revival of his sense of honor. "Not after—"

"Don't worry about that, Hunter. It's not exactly my money, it's—" He started to say that it was Lady Tarragon's, but stopped himself. This would not, he realized, be a tactful explanation. ". . . a kind of windfall. Due to unusual circumstances. You could go"—he recalled, somewhat hazily, his conversation months before with Dr. Purview— "you could go to Salem, Massachusetts. Or—" He paused. A possibility, an enticing possibility, had come to mind. "I can see you don't want to go back to Rome. But you liked Italy, didn't you, at first anyway? You could try Florence. That would be the best place to study Hawthorne anyway. That's where he was most of the time, wasn't it?"

Hunter nodded.

"Maybe you think you can't face Italy at all," Nick said, warming to his subject, "but it would be the best thing to do. You should get all these—frustrations out of your system." He paused, and added with the elated emphasis of one who has perceived an unexpected symmetry emerge from a tangled web of realities, "*Catharsis!* It would be catharsis, Hunter."

Hunter nodded again, noncommittally but with a slight

brightening of his features. Catharsis was not without appeal.

"And if you were studying Hawthorne there," Nick went on, "it would form an integrated pattern of therapy. Guilt themes," he added enthusiastically. "The relation between the moral and the aesthetic. You would have a truer understanding of Hawthorne than anybody has ever had. Original sin! Redemption!"

"Maybe. . . ." Hunter said. He paused, but there was no need for him to say anything more.

"I'll pay for your fare. Jet. And there'll be only one condition—when you publish the book, you use some other name. O.K.?"

"Well," Hunter said, "maybe. . . ."

The encounter was over. The victory was secure.

Nick put him in a taxi bound for the railroad station and began to congratulate himself. Almost immediately, however, as he watched the taxi drive off, he had misgivings. Suppose Hunter changed his mind on the way to the station. Suppose he had guilefully fallen in with Nick's plans to get away from him. It had all been too easy. Hunter might at that very moment be directing the taxi-driver to Dean Scarlett's house. Hunter, Nick judged, was slippery as well as stubborn.

As soon as these thoughts occurred to him he began to walk as rapidly as he could without attracting attention toward Muse Street.

It was Marian who answered the bell when he reached the house. She was a little surprised to see him, but he could tell at once from her manner that his fears had been groundless. Hunter had not put in an appearance. Cordially, she asked him to lunch, which was already on the table.

In other circles, his appearance at mealtime without any explained motive might have appeared either bold or eccentric. But at Parthenon, he knew, lunch was not much regarded—in contrast to dinner, which was an occasion for formal though thrifty hospitality—and motives for casual calls were not required. Parthenon specialized in motiveless droppings-in.

He accepted her invitation. As he entered the dining room, he felt a pang of regret that he could not tell her of the crises and triumphs of the morning. He wanted her to admire his resourcefulness in the disposal of Hunter. And the story would certainly dispel any notion she might have of him as a typical faculty member. But these were fruitless, if alluring, daydreams. Not for the first time he cursed the situation that prevented him from displaying to her his virtuosity and his depravity. Both would certainly have gratified her.

He shrugged off these imaginings and directed his attention to the topic of conversation that was engrossing Marian and her father. An undergraduate, it appeared, had been arrested the night before on a charge of breaking and entering a liquor store by the direct method of firing a pistol into the lock of its street door. As he listened to the Scarletts' measured views on this event his mind wandered again, to a consideration of their views if Hunter should, in fact, have appeared with his confession. His curiosity about Marian's reaction was intense.

She ate briskly and left them to return to her desk in Barrowes. But Dean Scarlett, lingered with Nick over the coffee. He was as usual disposed to a leisured examination of the abstract aspects of the topic.

"It's all most vexing," he said. "He was already drunk, of course."

"I hope so," Nick said.

"You hope so?" Dean Scarlett raised his eyebrows.

"I mean, we wouldn't like it if we thought our students broke into stores when they were sober. On the street, too. It wouldn't speak very well for their intelligence."

"No, I suppose not." Dean Scarlett's thin gray features twisted into a smile. "On the other hand, it doesn't speak very well for the atmosphere that we provide for them that they do it when drunk. I sometimes wonder if a college dormitory—or *a fortiori* a fraternity house—is not more calculated to prolong immaturity than to abbreviate it."

"Immaturity? I wouldn't say it was immature as much as"—Nick paused uncomfortably. His intended word was unpleasantly relevant to his own case, but there was nothing to do but say it—"criminal."

"In a technical sense you are right. But psychologically I think not. Of course this boy may be a genuine criminal. A certain percentage of them are bound to be. But I'm inclined to think that juvenile criminality is a universal phenomenon, more or less noticeable depending on the timidity of the individual and the degree of control that is exercised over him. As people grow up, most of them overcome their criminal tendencies, although a few do not. But a college tends in some ways to postpone their growing up, I think. The entire student body consists in this sense of criminals. Any group of young people does."

Nick nodded a little numbly. Once again Dean Scarlett had surprised him.

"I don't mean of course that all of them are totally without inhibitions. Or standards, if you prefer to call them that. They've acquired a few when they come—sometimes enough to keep them out of serious trouble. And they've acquired some more by the time they leave—if they hadn't, we ought all in conscience to resign. But the way we approach the task of supplying them with inhibitions is very defective. And for the most part they are not really interested in the sorts of inhibitions we're in business to purvey."

"Meaning"—Nick smiled somewhat self-consciously—"intellectual standards?"

The Dean refilled his coffee cup. He looked, Nick thought,

very tired and discouraged. "Yes. They are most of them not really accessible to intellectual standards. Which is not, naturally, their fault. It's the fault of their I.Q.s in some cases of course, but I'm more inclined to blame it on their parents. Their parents send them to college for the wrong reasons." He paused. "We reproach pet-owners with being anthropomorphic when they want dogs to behave like people. Well, I reproach parents with a rather similar defect of judgment. They want their sons to behave like themselves, and they mistakenly suppose that in college they will learn to do so. Which is the precise reverse of what the college is trying to teach them. What we want them to learn are ferocious and destructive things, how to verify footnotes and ridicule shibboleths. It's rather as if a dog-owner sent his dog to one of those military-training establishments where they teach them to go for the enemy's jugular, mistaking it for a decorous place where they learn to stand on their hind legs when ordered.

"And of course," he went on, plainly approaching a peroration, "it is our fault as well. For although we believe in what we preach we do not practice it in our own lives. Whether we like it or not, we are products of the same world as they; we impose conventional morality upon ourselves and upon the students. It is perhaps true that one cannot combine two different kinds of morality without on occasion appearing hypocritical. No doubt the young man apprehended for breaking locks will wonder when we take retributive measures against him whether we really believe that our only interest in him is the development of his mind, and of the scholarly virtues. If so, why should we suspend him, as we probably shall? There is no ready answer.

"The reason I have this on my mind is that I have had an interview with the young man's parents this morning."

"I see. Unpleasant?"

"Very, although not for the reasons one might expect. They took it calmly enough, as if it were the sort of thing that is to be expected, which I suppose it is. But they were perturbed at the possibility of his being removed from college. Most perturbed. They were prepared to go to almost any lengths to avoid it—mainly, I presume, out of a concern for appearances."

"Lengths? What lengths could they go to?"

"Money," Dean Scarlett said. "They offered a considerable sum to establish a fellowship. Very considerable."

"I see," Nick said. "What did you do with them?"

"I sent them to see the Director of Development, who takes care of these matters. He will send them to the President. It was a very considerable sum indeed. A natural thing for them to do, I suppose. And it's not bribery pure and simple—it combines the more attractive features of bribery and blackmail. If we don't accept the gift, they hint at retaliation."

"What kind of retaliation?"

"Vague, vague. Revelations of scandals. Their son appears to be in a position to inform them about scandals of various kinds on the campus. No doubt reliably."

Nick was silent. He had no personal sense of danger. The young man was in none of his classes or known to him personally; he could not possibly know anything about Dr. Stuart Hunter. But it seemed to Nick that the kind of negotiations he himself had been engaged in were not as unusual on the campus as he had supposed. To his surprise, he was shocked.

"But as I say," Dean Scarlett was continuing, "I am inclined to think that the fault lies with ourselves in some fashion. Even in the field in which we profess the greatest ethical rigor we sometimes pander to the world. As for example in the Schlotlaut matter."

"Schlotlaut?"

"You've not heard? An eminent visiting sociologist who has been invited to give lectures at the college. He is being paid for by Mr. Babcock, a trustee, who must be appeased in such matters."

"I've heard something about him. But I don't see why he should involve any compromise with—the world."

"He wouldn't if he were a man of real worth. But Pirbright informs me that he's a fraud and a fool. We shall permit him to speak anyway, to please Mr. Babcock. Mr. Babcock appears to think that Schlotlaut is God."

"Has Dean Pirbright met him, then?"

Dean Scarlett lowered his voice to a confidential whisper. "It's not generally known, but he has already arrived on the scene and is staying with Pirbright. He is allegedly conducting research and wishes to be incognito until it is complete. After that he will be publicly presented and will give the lectures. The whole proceedings smack of melodrama, or at least posturing. The very notion of an incognito scholar would appear to be a contradiction in terms. It would have been greatly preferable if Babcock had provided us with something frankly vulgar or popular. The cheap is greatly to be preferred to the meretricious."

Dean Scarlett rose from the table. "I must be getting back," he said. "Will you walk with me?"

They left the house and made their way toward the college.

"It was kind of you," the Dean said, "to come say goodbye."

"Goodbye?"

"I haven't spread it about that I'm going. It's no secret of course. But I'm a little ashamed of truancy."

"Truancy?"

"Not officially, of course. No doubt Marian told you that I'm going to attend a meeting of deans of students. A perfectly respectable reason. So respectable that the college is paying my way. But Los Angeles is a long way. Normally I shouldn't think of going."

"It ought to be a nice change." Nick said. "It's been a long winter."

"That," said Dean Scarlett, more hesitantly than ever, "is the point."

"To get some sun?"

"Yes. The real reason I'm going is that I need sun. Of course a week isn't very long, but by the time I get back the weather here ought to be better." He paused. "The doctor feels that a change of weather and some rest is advisable. I feel perfectly well, but he says I'm not."

"I'm sorry. I hope . . ."

"I hope not, too. No doubt the sun will take care of it. We all lead impossibly unwholesome lives in this impossibly unwholesome climate."

"When do you leave?"

"Tonight."

They had come to the point where their paths diverged and were standing still. Nick held out his hand.

"Have a good trip, sir."

"Thanks. I think I shall."

They parted. Nick continued on his way, reflectively kicking at twigs that lay on the path. He was so deeply preoccupied that he failed to note the safeguards that Dean Scarlett's trip provided. In California he would be safely out of reach if Hunter should change his mind before boarding a plane. Nick was, however, considering less cheerful aspects of his situation. He was thinking about bribery and blackmail.

Chapter XI   *Extracurricular Activities*

*I*n the week that followed the disposal of Stuart Hunter Nick found himself in a curious state of mind. His conversation with Dean Scarlett had had a peculiar effect. He was troubled by a curious feeling of disloyalty to the Dean personally and to some larger and more nebulous set of principles which the Dean embodied. An unpleasant sense of obligation to make some act of penance afflicted him. Bribery and blackmail were words that had once conveyed no moral message to him. Bribery and blackmail now had become very troubling words indeed. Sufficiently troubling to lead him to avoid the company of Marian Scarlett.

In this situation his chief solace was pride in his resourcefulness and a comforting conviction that the rest of the world was at least as corrupt as he. Even Dean Scarlett had pleaded guilty to moderate hypocrisy, a confession from which he tried to squeeze reassurance.

And certainly Nick's resourcefulness had been successful.

The cousin, his appearance made common knowledge by Parthenon's extraordinary facilities for news coverage, was accepted with condolence and without question. Nobody doubted his authenticity. Professor Nutter inquired about him with concern and, as the news spread, so did the rest of his colleagues. Nick was obliged (not without misgivings on practical grounds) to meet these solicitudes with a fictional rest home in Colorado and some rather impressionistic details of the course of psychotherapy there undertaken.

The demand for details continued to grow in an embarrassing fashion. Professor Nutter had, he himself said with every evidence of accuracy, been positively shaken by his encounter with the wild-eyed young man in the classroom. So, vicariously and with less probability, did Mrs. Nutter claim to have been shaken. So thoroughly did she disseminate colorful facts of his state that curiosity was aroused beyond the limits of convenience. The demented cousin became, along with the Zeta House and the assault on the liquor store, a *cause célèbre*. By degrees Nick was obliged to furnish him with ancestors, an unhappy love affair of a singularly seismic character, and in a moment of desperate verisimilitude with a doctor's degree. The alter ego as Professor Nutter was unhappily inspired to call him became, under pressure, almost indistinguishable from the ego. And these risky characterizations had to be interspersed with information, equally risky in a different way, about massive injections of vitamins, electric shock, and plenty of outdoor exercise.

In this general solicitude Nick's friends and contemporaries, the Messrs. Craig, Green, and Kelly, did not share. They were inclined to be sportive rather than solicitous in their reactions, and they were incurious about the background information for which others, particularly faculty wives, displayed so voracious an appetite. This was just as

well. Nick had a strong feeling that the parallelisms would
be less readily swallowed by the Messrs. Craig, Green, and
Kelly than by, say, Eunice Nutter. They were far too
strongly disposed toward critical analysis. But the interest
of these three scholars was directed elsewhere: Mike was
more distracted than ever by his attentions to Mrs. Purview
and by a sullen concern with public reactions to them, and
Brandon and Sid were distracted by Mike's position. They
were afraid, they told Nick, that affairs were moving toward a climax that would dwarf anything else that had
happened at Parthenon that year.

The two of them had called on Nick to discuss the matter, and he was hospitably providing them with Scotch
whiskey. "The trouble is," Brandon said, "he's such a weird
idiot. If he were a fool about everything, one could attack
him via his folly. But he isn't. He always sees where you're
leading and won't discuss it. It's like trying to point out to
an architect the perils of building castles in the air."

"He knows what's going on all right—that people are
talking more and more," Nick said, remembering the trip to
Albany.

"He has a death wish," Sid said. "He wants to be proved
right at his own expense so that he can complain about how
unjust the world is. It's beyond his powers to let the world
be unjust without taking it upon himself to martyrize himself as an object lesson. Although, since he thinks everyone
is totally corrupt, what good a revelation of corruptness
is going to do I don't know. The fact is, I sometimes think
he's doing it merely to provide proof of universal corruption. I find it difficult to suppose he actually is fond of the
creature."

"You're wrong." Brandon was both brusque and somber. "He is. The first time he saw that glorious face, his
eyes lit up with the dark fires of illicit aspiration. Partly
just because of the way she looks, I suppose. But partly be-

cause he regards her as a fellow-victim. I grant you that
it's a transference or tension-satisfaction or whatever the
hell they call it, in that sense. He is drawn to her as a fellow-victim."

"What of?" Nick asked.

"Society. Don't ask me why Mike regards himself as a
victim but he does. His father beat him, maybe, or he
nourished socially unacceptable longings for his Aunt Ur-
sula, or something. And what he is phenomenologically, if
that's the right word, she is by any objective standard.
Everything in her life has been a crucifixion of one sort or
another. So naturally when he saw her tragic beauty and
heard those melodious accents of martyrdom, a tingling
vibration was instantly set up. He probably never met anybody else before who was so thoroughly and obviously a
victim."

"You mean, he felt sorry for her."

"O.K., Stuart. In English that's what I mean. But no
more for her than for himself."

"What does old Purview know, do you think?"

"God knows." Sid shrugged his shoulders. "One would
guess him incapable of noticing anything, but if he happened to, one would also guess that he wouldn't concern
himself much with it. The complaisant buffoon. The senile
cuckold. A type well-known in literature, I am told. I might
be wrong, but I think it's not him Mike needs to worry
about. He won't make any scenes, I imagine. The worst
one can expect from him is a quiet termination of the appointment. What matters is public opinion at large. Give
me a drink."

"But if everybody knows, and nothing has happened
yet . . . ?" Nick poured out whiskey as he spoke.

"The trouble is," Brandon said, also holding out his glass,
"Mike is right. Everyone *is* corrupt. Sid laughs at the idea,
but it's very serious. They like thrills, damn them, even if

they have to build them out of nothing. Just one incident
and the fruity whispers will become shrieks of outraged
horror. You aren't in a position to know about the exhilarating atmosphere of moral indignation that enveloped this
place when one of the undergraduates was so ill-advised
as to make improper advances to a middle-aged lady named
Pilkington in the cataloguing department. I speak, incidentally, in both a geographical and a professional sense.
The locus of the crime was also the scene of the lady's
vocational pursuits. She'd stayed after hours to catch up
on a backlog of Dewey Decimals."

"So what happened?"

"Full statement on situation, widely distributed, by hor-
rified victim. Wild cries of horror from Acropolis press and
subsequently from alumni, trustees, parents, and other
friends of Parthenon. The word 'rape,' wholly inapplicable
to actual events, gradually and chillingly attached to incident. Threat of police proceedings rumored. Terror on part
of administration. Student disposed of. End of incident,
except for bitter feuds among faculty and administration
arising out of it, for reasons I've never understood, since
practically everybody seemed to agree on the merits of the
case. The point is, the student was canned without hearing
and without any discussion at all. There's no doubt that
something similar would happen if somebody lit a fuse
under Mike and Elsa."

This graphic recitation confirmed Nick's comforting hypothesis that Parthenon was as immoral as he was. But
still he felt as though he were being slowly compressed by
the application of heavy weights. He saw no reason to dis-
pute Brandon's analysis of the crisis, or his sardonic appraisal of local opinion's capacity to exploit sensations, but
this was a twist in the world's corruption that threatened
instead of reassuring him. The story contained one particularly alarming suggestion. He hadn't thought before about

police proceedings. The possibility suddenly occurred to him that his activities were technically as well as morally criminal. The idea jeopardized the only consolation he had previously been able to draw—that when exposure came, he would simply depart from the scene. Would it, he wondered feverishly, be worth consulting a lawyer? The idea had to be dismissed as soon as it came to him. His was not a problem that could be easily explained to a lawyer.

He sat bolt upright in his chair in the course of these reflections. Fortunately Sid Green was talking intently. "I'm not absolutely sure you're right, Brandon, although your principle is undoubtedly sound. But you omit one of the outstanding characteristics of the local culture pattern, which is capriciousness. You can never tell how Parthenon will behave. It's not altogether impossible that the reaction would be one of frozen horror, and frozen horror by itself never did anybody any harm. Responses are never proportionate to causes around here. Compare, for example, the question of the stuffed crocodile, a *cause célèbre* for generations, with the Hindmire affair, which nobody ever mentions. The crocodile business was completely trivial.

"Objectively considered, the capriciousness is very unsettling. You can't tell when an eruption is going to take place. Think of the three of us: I take it that our lives are relatively blameless aside from recurrent intoxication, but there's no way of guaranteeing that some stupendous crisis might not at any moment engulf any of us. I don't worry quite as much about Mike's problems as you do—the bell may be tolling for thee. At this very moment horrifying revelations are quite possibly being made about you or me or Stu that could blast us higher than Mike."

Nick's sense of compression was intensified. He was not, however, aware of its very exact timing. For as Sid had casually suggested, at that very moment, by Pacific Standard Time, precisely such revelations were about to be made.

They were about to be made in a dimly lit bar called the Avocado Room, a place designed for the relaxation and festivity of patrons of the Desert Springs Hotel. The Avocado Room offered an atmosphere both unfamiliar and distasteful to Dean Scarlett. Its decoration and the almost total absence of illumination that cloaked it in hypothetical glamour gave him the impression that he was a character in a third-rate film about underworld violence. He would have been glad to leave, but he was here by appointment to meet his friend Dr. Campion, and he was bound to await him surrounded by these intimations of drama among the criminal classes.

His restlessness was presently distracted by an enthusiastic greeting from a dimly visible newcomer to the Avocado Room who addressed him as "Pinky," an ancient nickname deriving not from any pertinent quality of his hair or complexion but from his surname. This souvenir of a youth long since lost did nothing to dispel the effect which his surroundings had had upon him.

"Arthur," he said with all the heartiness he could command, but with the sudden misgivings common to people who, after arranging meetings with old friends, wonder whether the oldness is not likely to have vitiated the friendship. He stood up. "Arthur, it's good to see you." In two ways the statement fell short of accuracy: he was not absolutely sure that it was good, and given the darkness he could see Dr. Campion only in vague outline.

"Well, Pinky. It's great good luck that you wrote me you were coming West. Otherwise I should certainly not have bothered to attend the hummingbird convention."

He sat down and ordered drinks for them both, commenting upon the happy accident that had brought about simultaneous assemblages of Deans of Students and hummingbird enthusiasts in cities only fifty miles apart. "Normally," he said, "I don't come to the hummingbird do's, especially since it's a particularly bad time for me. But it's a fine excuse for a trip and to see you. I'm surprised *you* came. It's a long way to come for a meeting of Deans."

Dean Scarlett looked consideringly at his sherry, which he was finding of poor quality. "I wouldn't under ordinary circumstances, but this year I wanted some sun. The College pays my way so it seemed a good opportunity. It's been a rather bad winter at home."

"How is Marian? And Ethel?"

"Marian is fine. Ethel is as usual. How is Clarissa?"

"Clarissa is very well. She has taken up paper folding."

"She has done what?"

"Paper folding. It's a Japanese art. Very delicate and difficult."

"Ah." Dean Scarlett felt an overwhelming lack of interest in the delicacy of paper folding, and he was a little afraid from Dr. Campion's manner that he might be going to hear a detailed statement on it. He was desperately tired, and he wished now that the appointment had been arranged for some open-air spot or at least some bar with a setting less darkly glamorous than the Avocado Room. But he felt it necessary to make an effort. "I have heard," he said a little archly, "something about a Baptist minister."

"You have heard what?"

The conversation was most unsatisfactory. Neither party seemed able to progress. Paper folding had proved infertile, and the Baptist minister seemed to be perplexing. It had probably been a mistake to bring up the Baptist minister at all, Dean Scarlett decided wearily, but now there was nothing to do but to pursue the subject through embarrassing explanations.

"What Baptist minister?" There was something at once anxious and impatient in Dr. Campion's voice suggesting a suspicion that his old friend had grown senile.

Dean Scarlett sighed and tried again. "I heard something about Clarissa's going out with a Baptist minister."

"With a Baptist *minister?*" Dr. Campion asked blankly. "I don't know anything about it. What gave you that idea?"

It had been a disastrous mistake. Dean Scarlett retreated. "Perhaps I misunderstood. It was something that your young friend Hunter said. But no doubt I have it wrong."

"Yes, I think you do. How *is* Hunter?" Dr. Campion's tones were distinctly cold.

"Fine. He's a tremendous success."

"Is he indeed?"

"We're most grateful to you people for sending him to us. I think he's going to do wonders for our English Department, which could do with some wonders."

"You have gotten to know Hunter well?"

"Moderately well. I've taken some interest in him because of your recommendation and I think very well of him. Marian sees something of him, too, so he's been around the house quite often."

"*Marian* sees something of him?"

"Yes. I don't know that there's anything in it—"

"I think I ought to tell you," Dr. Campion said, "that Hunter has behaved very badly toward Clarissa. There was—well, I should call it an understanding between them, before he went to Rome. Then last summer he suddenly stopped writing. She has heard nothing since. To speak quite frankly, as a father I find his conduct unforgivable. I think that Marian ought to be warned."

This distressing revelation brought forcibly and disagreeably to Dean Scarlett's mind his conversation months earlier with Hunter on the subject of Clarissa. Hunter's curious evasiveness was now explained. The invention of the Baptist minister must, he regretfully thought, be taken as indicating not only a lack of honesty but positive frivolity in concealing his own derelictions. This was shocking. It was alarming for Marian's sake, but more than Marian's feelings were involved. A young man so injudicious—to put no more pejorative a word to it—was certainly a risk in larger ways. He might eventually be expected to involve everyone in some major unpleasantness. Dean Scarlett, his mind rapidly traversing the history of such crises at Parthenon, was led to an anxious question. "I suppose that there's no doubt about his professional competence? And scholarly promise? You have had no reason to revise your high opinion on those points?"

Dr. Campion considered.

"No, I suppose not. I confess to being very angry with him, although it is naturally a subject I don't discuss with most people. But I have no reason to doubt his competence. The literature people felt as I do that his work was thorough and intelligent, although a little unimaginative. Naïve, I think, was the criticism that his supervisor made of him. And I shouldn't be surprised if naïveté were the trouble with his character as well. To be perfectly fair, one might say that he found himself embroiled in a situation he disliked, changed his mind, and had neither the poise nor the wit to think of anything except the easy and rather contemptible way out which he chose, of breaking it off through inaction. He is certainly a rather inexperienced young man in worldly matters."

"Inexperienced?" Dean Scarlett, who had been listening in growing bewilderment, frowned. "I should not have said inexperienced, especially not in worldly matters. I can conceive of his being irresponsible. Violent perhaps. But not inexperienced."

Dr. Campion was also puzzled. "Certainly naïve though. And he's a coward, I'm afraid, judging from his treatment of Clarissa. I know that it's very old-fashioned to judge character from physiognomy, but even before that happened I used to wonder sometimes about his chin. He has a very weak chin, if you've noticed."

"A weak chin?" It was Dean Scarlett's turn to consider that perhaps his old friend, overcome by labors on behalf of generations of graduate students and of hummingbird research, had fallen victim to some form of premature mental cloudiness that led him to confuse one promising young graduate student with another.

"He led a very sheltered life until he went to Rome. He is a type, I imagine, who might easily be caught up by Old World decadence." Dr. Campion stated this somewhat old-fashioned notion with the conviction of a man whose reading has not carried him into an era much more recent than that of Henry James. "He is certainly very impressionable. One might say callow."

Dean Scarlett's frown deepened, as did his belief that Dr. Campion was in the throes of senility. "Sheltered?" he asked numbly. "Impressionable? *Callow?*"

"Why do you keep repeating things, Pinky?" Dr. Campion's doubts as to his friend's mental alertness were also deepening. "Of course he's impressionable and callow. All that blue-eyed boyishness."

"Blue-eyed boyishness?"

Dr. Campion's concern mounted further, but so did his impatience. "Do stop it, Pinky. Certainly blue-eyed boyishness."

"But Hunter is very dark. You have him mixed up, Arthur. Of course, I realize that it's been some time since you last saw him. So many graduate students pass through your hands. . . ." He was now positively solicitous. "Of course we all get confused among our old students—nobody could hope to keep them all straight."

"I can keep Hunter straight all right. Blue-eyed and boyish."

"Black eyes," Dean Scarlett said slowly and patiently.

"Black hair. Very broad-shouldered. Looks a little like a prizefighter."

"Spectacles?" Dr. Campion was clearly uncertain now. "Horn-rimmed spectacles?"

"No, no spectacles." Dean Scarlett was soothing. "Latin in appearance. One might say tough, perhaps. His language is not altogether grammatical, which I take to be an affectation. Colloquial. Very definitely colloquial. A deep voice."

"No." Dr. Campion's manner was changing. He spoke in tones not of contradiction but of elucidation, and spoke a little faintly, as if fighting his way toward consciousness after a sharp blow on the head. "A rather high-pitched voice. He speaks very precisely, almost pendantically. Blond straight hair. Crew-cut, the last time I saw him. Pale-blue eyes, very round."

Dean Scarlett, his manner also changed, stared in horror. He was pale, and he emptied the glass of unpalatable sherry at one draught. For a moment they both sat in silence. Communication between them was no longer difficult; for the moment it was simply unnecessary. Their minds were racing along identical courses. But Dean Scarlett's was the quicker and more subtle of the two, and being accustomed to explore every avenue he was, as Marian had once observed, sometimes led into rather peculiar ones. The effect of the Avocado Room now began to make itself felt upon Dean Scarlett's judgment. He spoke with some difficulty.

"Do you—do you think he may have murdered him?" In his agitation his grasp of pronouns had lost its usual precision, but his meaning was clear enough.

"Well, really." Despite his words, Dr. Campion did not appear to reject the suggestion out of hand. "No one murders anyone to secure an instructorship at Parthenon."

"If he's not dead, where is he?"

"He may have been paid off. He's probably still in Europe."

"But *a fortiori*, why would anybody pay anybody off to secure an instructorship at Parthenon?"

"There's probably some perfectly innocent explanation, Pinky."

"How could there be an innocent explanation? The fact in itself is proof that the explanation must be guilty. There must be some—racket." He pronounced the word gingerly. "A *ring* of some kind," he added, "with its headquarters at Parthenon. What better lair than a college? No one would ever think to look for the headquarters of a ring on a college campus. Narcotics seems most likely. And undoubtedly murder as well."

"You say he's Latin in appearance. Italian, would you say?"

"Decidedly."

"Or Sicilian?"

Dean Scarlett caught his meaning. "The Mafia?"

"What ought we to do? It may be rather dangerous for anyone who interferes." Dr. Campion looked covertly around the room as if expecting to find agents of nameless rings lurking in the imitation avocado trees.

Dean Scarlett considered. Dr. Campion's affrighted glance had restored his sense of proportion. There was, he now obliged himself to recognize, no doubt that the glamour of the setting, the atmosphere of inferior films of intrigue, had had an unwholesome effect on the two aging scholars. They were unquestionably infected by melodrama. It was hard, to be sure, to construct any explanation that was not melodramatic. The conditions seemed to preclude any explanation not, in fact, criminal. But there was no absolute evidence that the crime was of a sensational nature. A measure of scholarly detachment reasserted itself. Dean Scarlett was whiter than ever, but when he spoke it was in something more resembling the dispassionate tones of a Dean of Students amply experienced in all forms of waywardness.

"Of course, you're quite right, Arthur. We must not allow our imaginations to carry us away. There is very likely a simple, although I should doubt an innocent, explanation." Further soothed by his own words, he continued more hopefully, "A practical joke of some elaborate sort, perhaps."

"No, Pinky. I do not see how it could be a joke."

"In one sense it certainly is." His sense of humor also returning, Dean Scarlett laughed, although weakly. "A joke on us and on Parthenon. A most formidable one. I should think quite unique. We are certainly very gullible. Of course, whoever he is he must have had some academic training, but still he has put it over with quite astonishing skill. We have all been made fools of. Seen from that angle it certainly is a joke." He paused. "But whatever it is, I shall have to go to the President at once. I daresay he will think I am demented."

Dean Scarlett contemplated the possibility pensively. "It would be best to try to clarify things before I speak to the President," he went on. "I must have some further information before I can hope to make him take the matter seriously—and he will require it, of course, when he goes to the police. I shall send a telegram to—ah—the young man in question before I board the plane tomorrow. I shall ask him to meet me tomorrow night, immediately after I reach home. Then I shall see the President the next morning."

"I shouldn't mention any—suspicions in the telegram. It would be safer not to. And I should arrange to have somebody with you when you see him."

"Come, Arthur." Dean Scarlett assumed a slight air of patronage. "Let's not be melodramatic. But there is certainly no need to arouse his suspicions in advance. I shall

simply ask him to call at my house tomorrow evening—"
He broke off. "I think I shall have another glass of that
sherry," he said.

On the following evening Marian Scarlett awaited her
father's return with some impatience. The days of his absence had been trying ones, and she found herself unwontedly depressed. Her mother had been somewhat more de-
manding, perhaps a little more genuinely unwell, since his
departure. Even beyond that, however, she had not realized how difficult it would be to face the tedium of lonely
evenings.

She had expected the evenings to be enlivened by calls
from Stuart Hunter. Or more precisely, she now told herself, she had been counting on them. But he had not come,
and when she met him on the campus he had greeted her
with an absent, even an evasive, manner. He had looked as
if he were preoccupied with some inward melancholy of
his own. But this seemed to her so markedly out of character that she dismissed it. She was obliged to conclude that
he was avoiding her company, and this she found exasperating.

A determined effort at reasonable analysis forced her
to confess that she had no grounds for exasperation. If he
were avoiding her it was, she ruthlessly informed herself,
her own fault. Her conduct in the past few months must
certainly seem to a detached observer—or, what was of
greater importance, to an observer who was not detached
—to fall into the detestable category of the coy and the
trifling. This conclusion was not only humiliating; it also
drove home the fact that her course of conduct had failed
in its purpose. It had been a mistake to suppose that the
way to reduce the attractiveness of a man whom she found
disturbing was to neutralize it by keeping impersonal company with him. And with still greater ruthlessness, she now

confessed to herself that she had never really made that supposition.

She was ready to confess that she had behaved badly and foolishly. And much more, she was ready to abandon her ideas of escape. The idea of escape, or at least of escape from anything more than the house on Muse Street, appeared now in the light of childish folly. Stuart Hunter, even a Stuart Hunter who was a doctor of philosophy, she was courageously prepared to accept on any terms.

But what seemed regrettably clear was that he was no longer prepared to be accepted. She found herself in the classic position of a woman who has hesitated too long, and the very triteness of her position further oppressed her. She was a woman who had prided herself upon an emotional life free of triteness.

As she prepared to take up her mother's tray, she looked about her at the parlor, with its symbols of incarceration—the green bronze lamp, the Homeric painting, the brasses on the mantelpiece, alien, permanent, imprisoning.

It was while she stood staring inimically about her that the telephone rang. She put down the tray and went to answer it. In the moment before she lifted the receiver certain impressions crossed her mind, the more rapid and vivid for her mood. There was nothing to do, there would never be anything to do, but go about the business of the household. Of carrying trays and answering telephones, of polishing from time to time with liturgical solicitude and a soft cloth the symbols of imprisonment on the mantelpiece. Quiet and hard-working, uncomplaining, sensible, she would go on until she died.

She sighed, a sigh of sheer resignation, as she took up the phone.

"Hello?"

"Miss Marian Scarlett, please. Long distance is calling."

"This is she."

"This is Miss Marian Scarlett?"

"Yes."

"Go ahead, please."

There were mild electronic noises. A man's voice again asked if this were Marian Scarlett.

She had thought it would be her father, although what his purpose might be in calling she could not guess. Instead the voice said, "This is Horace Zantzinger. I am Dean at Monroe College. A friend of your father's."

"Yes?"

"I have some bad news, I'm afraid."

"Yes?" She had already guessed it.

"Your father has been taken ill. In the airport this morning, just as he was about to leave."

"Seriously?"

"He is in the hospital. But they don't think it's critical."

"What happened?"

She felt nothing beyond a sort of breathlessness, almost of exhaustion, as if she had just run a long distance.

"He had a stroke. I gather he hadn't been very well?"

"No."

"As I say, they are very hopeful at the hospital. There's no immediate danger. I didn't call you before, because I wanted to wait until they told me something definite. But I am sure now, for the present at least, there's nothing to—" He stopped.

"I see." She was summoning her resources, trying to shake off the peculiar tiredness which was paralyzing her. "I had better come out at once, I suppose. I shall have to make some arrangements about my mother, but. . . ."

"I don't think it's necessary, Miss Scarlett. There is nothing you can do at present. He's not conscious. They say he may not be for some time. Days, perhaps. I called your mother's sister in San Diego. I happened to remember she lived there. She is coming up tomorrow. I'll stay until she arrives."

"I see." She paused. "Can you tell me anything more?"

He told her, but there was not much more.

"Your aunt will call you tomorrow," he concluded. "Don't worry."

She hung up, considering the practicalities. He was quite right, of course. There was no reason for her to go at the moment. The practicalities were against it. There would be plenty to do here. Her mother. And the President must be notified, and relatives. But her whole personality reacted against the thought of staying. It would be better not to say anything tonight to her mother. That would make it easier to get done the other things that would have to be done. With a sleeping pill her mother would shortly be unconscious, and in the morning could be told. She was stronger and more reasonable in the morning, and Marian would have a chance to . . . She would take up the tray now and say nothing. Or at least she would do it in a moment.

She looked around the room, now more than ever a prison. But she saw with the surprise of someone watching the ingenious transformation of a stage set that it had already begun to change. The immutable symbols, the inexorable fetters, were disintegrating. Nothing was there now except the shabby and transient trivialities of a past already finished. The fringed curtains would come down and the painting would be thrown away and the incense-burner and the candlesticks would turn black with tarnish, and the house itself, the impregnable prison, would be laid bare to its crumbling mortar. The ugly, pathetic little objects that it contained were already half forgotten in a fog of memories. The room was already gray with neglect and decay. It lay around her silent and meaningless, a display of junk in a secondhand store.

TWO

A sudden nostalgia for faraway things took hold of her
as if she had remembered some childhood possession long
lost and forgotten, for which she felt a powerful and unreasonable longing. She put her hands together tightly, as
if by pressing them she could strengthen her spirit for the
jobs to be done, and she stood for a moment without moving, looking into time. Quiet, hard-working, and sensible.

It was the doorbell that saved her from a species of
trance in which she might have stood with her fingernails
cutting into her palms for some indefinite period. She went
to answer it automatically, as she had gone to answer the
telephone.

"Stuart!" He was on the doorstep. She looked at him
wonderingly. His presence was a surprise of a magnitude
that she could grasp, an event in the comprehensible realm,
more real than the telephone message. She was overwhelm-
ingly glad to see him. It was only by an effort that she
prevented herself from running to him and throwing herself into his arms. Then she saw that he himself was in
some very considerable state of perplexity. He must somehow have heard the news and come to offer her his help.

"You've heard?" she said.

He nodded. "Your father is home. I had a telegram this
morning. He told me to come here."

"Home?" It was a moment before she could grasp what
he had said. She stared at him appalled, and with difficulty spoke. "Then you haven't heard."

His face softened in confusion, and he too seemed to be
speaking with difficulty. "Heard?"

"He's been taken ill. In Los Angeles. He wired me, too;
he seems to have decided to come home early, but he had
a stroke. He is in the hospital. Unconscious."

"You mean—"

"I don't know," Marian said. "They say they think he

247

isn't going to die. At least not at once." She found a certain satisfaction in this bald phrasing.

"How did you find out?"

"I had a phone call a few minutes ago."

He spoke softly now. "What can I do, Marian?"

"I must call the President, and I have got to take Mother's tray up, and—"

"I'll call the President."

"Thank you. I must take the tray up. Mother's had a bad day." The words, spoken automatically, struck her as grotesque. Her mother, with her inevitable bad days, had had a worse one. She laughed aloud at the incongruity of what was happening. Her father, the strong, the invulnerable, the dominant. . . . She laughed again, senselessly and dangerously, and then she was in Nick's arms crying, with the emotions of her lifetime unleashed in the security of his hands.

Chapter XII   Social Life

The President and Mrs. Overton were At Home again.

It was Mrs. Overton's greatest joy to perform the duties of her position in the matter of official entertaining, and the more frequent the occasions for performing them, the more joyful she was. Although giving receptions constituted, as she often observed to her friends, an exhausting responsibility as well as a *privilege,* she gave as many of them as possible. They were the most useful form of official entertaining, she thought, since they enabled her to cast the widest possible net. And in one respect they involved responsibilities slighter than dinner parties, the principal alternative. As Mrs. Nutter was fond of pointing out to everybody who didn't know it and to most who did, the College paid for receptions.

The weeks before the Easter vacation were normally a period in which Mrs. Overton was unable to perform her duty about receptions. Entertaining during Lent was not approved. This year, however, a special circumstance was thought to justify an interruption of such disciplines. Dr. Schlotlaut was ready to emerge from his incognito. Both courtesy and Mr. Babcock required a formal presentation of the visiting lecturer to the faculty and to that group described by Mrs. Overton as "the wider community."

There was some momentary hesitation, on the part of the President rather than his wife, about the propriety of such a celebration at a time when the Dean of Students was in a coma in Los Angeles. To this protest, tentatively proposed, Mrs. Overton had replied with the reasonable view that they would not consider the illness of an instructor as grounds for abandoning a reception and that it was therefore pure snobbery to do so in the case of a higher-ranking dignitary. And, she had added, since nobody knew how long he might stay in a coma, it would be foolish to consider postponing it on Dean Scarlett's account. Cards were accordingly distributed, and a week after the Dean's attack the reception took place.

The occasion was auspicious from the point of view of conversation. The faculty, like any other group whose members meet one another almost every day, was always pleased to meet again. Among them there was no dearth of subjects for discussion. And the trustees, who presented a much more formidable social problem, since they were known only slightly and were regarded with a chilling combination of apathy, awe, and dislike by most of the faculty, might now be drawn into talk about the evocative presence of Dr. Schlotlaut or the deplorable state of Dean Scarlett and the dramatic developments related to it which had recently occurred. These were stimulating and perfectly respectable topics. Under normal circumstances respectable topics of any sort were hard to find.

Mrs. Overton, fully aware of the unusual advantages thus provided, was sedulously exploiting them in the reception line. She remarked graciously upon one or the other, alternately, to each guest.

Nick approached the receiving line as he had approached most other things in the past week, in a mood both thoughtful and perplexed. His position with Marian Scarlett was now drastically altered. Following the evening when he had presented himself at Muse Street in response to her father's still unexplained telegram, the alterations had been palpable. That night, with his sensitivities taut and despite the painful circumstances of his visit, he had instantly understood the change that had taken place in her attitude. But for the moment anyway, that change simplified nothing in *his* life. However welcome, it merely complicated further the increasing complexities of morals and practicalities in which he was trapped. His odd sense of obligation to the College prevented flying with her to some distant and secure spot. And even if it had not, flight would of necessity have to be prefaced with confession, and he was still uncertain about her reactions to confession. False pretenses, she had told him on Christmas Day, were the one unforgivable crime.

But even these difficulties paled into insignificance before a more immediate, if less basic, one. Her father's condition and the astonishing change in the Scarlett household that had followed it imposed delay. It was no moment, clearly, for attempts to clarify his and Marian's situation, even if he had been sure of how to go about doing so. To attempt it now would suggest an effort to take advantage of an anguishing turn in her affairs.

For Nick himself the turn in affairs had been painful enough. He was genuinely and deeply disturbed by the illness of a man whom he had come to regard with something approaching awe as the embodiment of principles that he as yet only dimly understood. And this feeling added another dimension to his mood as he approached the reception line, a dimension of extreme irritation. Parthenon's tendency to convert misfortunes into sensations was as clearly illustrated by its reaction to Dean Scarlett's illness as by the reaction which Brandon and Sid expected to greet a public exposure of Mike Kelly's private life. The corruption to which they had so forcefully referred was now being revealed, in minor key. Parthenon, buzzing exuberantly with the news from California and from Muse Street, was very irritating indeed.

Mrs. Overton's presence irritated him still further. Her first words, spoken in tones of one enjoying an apocalypse, summarized all the things Nick disliked about her.

"He is here," she said dramatically.

"That's nice."

"*Most* distinguished. *You* will be especially interested to meet him. He knows everybody in Europe."

Nick acknowledged with a bow the impressiveness of so large an acquaintance.

"You are sure to have friends in common," she went on. "He mentioned knowing the titular Bishop of Ephesus. We are so privileged." Graciously, she nodded him on to make way for the next arrival, whispering ecstatically as he moved on, "One calls him Herr Professor Doctor."

She turned to greet the next comer with her alternate formula. "Isn't it sad about Dean Scarlett? But marvellous about The Miracle!"

Nick found himself washed by the crowd into the lap of Mrs. Freeman, the Bursar's wife, with whom he had a slight acquaintance.

"Mrs. Overton was just talking about The Miracle," she said. "She said to me, 'Annette, what God takes with one hand he gives with the other.'" Mrs. Freeman spoke vigorously but with a slight lisp and an almost complete absence of intonation. "But I told her, 'It's not God, Claudia, it's Sigmund Freud.' I tell you, Dr. Hunter, when I heard that Ethel Scarlett had gotten out of bed and gone to California to take care of William, I said to my husband, 'Rudyard, it's a pity he didn't have a stroke years ago. It's the only thing that could get Ethel out of bed.'"

"I said to Rudyard," she went on, her brightly painted lips curling back from pointed teeth, "'They ain't a never gonna come home no more.'" She paused, laughing gaily at this excursion into dialect. "Once Ethel's got him out of Acropolis and into bed where she can manage him, she's going to keep him there forever."

"I hear he's better," Nick said weakly.

"I was talking to the President a minute ago, and he said, 'Annette, the latest report from the doctors is that he won't be able to resume the Deanship.' I told him, 'Helm, Parthenon's loss is Ethel Scarlett's gain.'" Mrs. Freeman stopped and then abruptly went on, like a geyser given to gushing at brief but regular intervals. "The one *I* feel sorry for is Marian."

She chattered on. His attention wandered, then returned. ". . . while the old folks are sitting in rocking chairs in California having the time of their lives," she was saying, concluding some dissertation on Marian's plight. She paused. The fountain of her discourse subsided, but almost at once a new one immediately surged forth. "Tell me, Dr. Hunter, about your cousin. I hope he's better. I said to my husband, 'Rudyard, there isn't anything in the world sadder than when somebody in your family goes crazy!'"

They were now joined, to Nick's relief, by a third person, an instructor of Fine Arts drifting rudderless through the crowd, whose arm was powerfully grasped by Mrs. Freeman. "You know Dr. Hunter," she said. "Dr. Carmickle. We were just talking about the sad case of Dr. Hunter's cousin, Dr. Carmickle. The one who's gone off his rockers."

"Oh, indeed?" Dr. Carmickle, a pale and embarrassed

young man, looked as if he had doubts about the propriety of this topic.

"I was just talking to Mr. Appleyard, that trustee who looks like Fatty Arbuckle, about it. He said to me, 'Mrs. Freeman, it's the saddest thing in the world.' How is he, Dr. Hunter?"

"He has very good care," Nick said judiciously. He avoided predicting any positive recovery for the cousin. You never knew when a chronic derangement might come in handy.

"It isn't by any chance that place near Pueblo, the Rancho del Salud?" Mrs. Freeman asked. "I knew someone years ago who had a very good experience there. But it was catarrh in her case, of course. She wasn't nervous. Everybody was so sympathetic with you when we heard he'd been here. I certainly hope he gets better. I said to Rudyard's aunt just the other day, 'Aunt Chloë, if you think things are going to get better, they will.' 'It ain't gonna rain no more' is my philosophy."

And with this motto Mrs. Freeman moved away, leaving Nick with Dr. Carmickle, who regarded him with what seemed to be sympathy. This was not surprising. They had spoken only occasionally, but he had gathered that Dr. Carmickle was an exceptionally determined intellectual, unlikely to have much enthusiasm for Mrs. Freeman's vagaries. Confirming this guess, Dr. Carmickle glanced at her departing form and said, "In the *cinquecento* they'd have poisoned that female out of hand."

Nick laughed. "In the Villa Sfiduzia in Terni," he said genially, "they show you a room where Guido di Diffidenza poisoned three of his wives because they got on his nerves."

"Ah." Dr. Carmickle brightened. "You know the Villa Sfiduzia? So few people ever get there. It's a real treasure."

"I know the Diffidenzas. They used to ask us—that is, me —for weekends."

"The *graffiature!*" Dr. Carmickle said. "The *graffiature* in the private dungeon! You know them?"

"Yes." Nick was slightly embarrassed.

"The finest pornographic art in central Italy!" Dr. Carmickle spoke with the quiet enthusiasm of a dedicated scholar. "If it could be reproduced in book form, everybody would go to the Villa Sfiduzia."

This seemed to Nick a probably accurate statement but one better not explored in the hearing of trustees. He attempted a change of subject. "They make their own honey, too. It's very good."

"The Sfiduzia *graffiature,*" Dr. Carmickle went on, "are absolutely unique. The line form undoubtedly derives from the younger Platenius."

"So they said." It seemed respectable enough to discuss the Sfiduzia *graffiature* on this abstract plane. "But it looked to me as if whoever did them had been looking at some of Briosaccio's *predelle* in Arezzo.

"Briosaccio, eh?" Dr. Carmickle spoke absently. He stared thoughtfully, then assumed an expression of intense interest and concentration. "Briosaccio, you think? The *predelle* in Arezzo. Yes, I know them. That's rather an exciting thought, Hunter. There is undoubtedly something reminiscent. 'Bacchus.' The sundial *iconografia!* What a remarkably interesting idea. But do you think that the tactile values . . . ?"

"Yes, I do." Nick spoke emphatically, although privately uncertain about the tactile values.

"Yes, yes." Dr. Carmickle, normally a somewhat doughy personality, was catching fire. "I see exactly what you mean. The tactile values . . ."

"Yes."

"And of course, the composition tonality. A most original idea, Hunter." He paused, and asked with greater restraint, "Have you considered writing it up?"

"No, I haven't." Recalling the customary formula for such matters, Nick added, "Not my field, you know."

"No, I suppose not. It is a most interesting thought. I might possibly do a little—thinking along these lines myself. If you're not planning to do anything with it yourself, of course."

"It's all yours," Nick said generously.

"I must think about this," Dr. Carmickle said with ebullience. "I really must." And unexpectedly he disappeared, apparently in haste to commence a learned exploration of the matter.

Nick looked after him, surprised equally by the suddenness of his departure and the intensity of his reaction to Nick's views on the derivation of the Sfiduzia *graffiature*. The latter was the latest in a series of lessons in the extent of his own attainments that had begun with his first visit to Muse Street. His information might be somewhat scattered, but he was from time to time startled to find how much it impressed other people.

His reflections were interrupted by the President, who came up on him unexpectedly from behind.

"Have you met Schlotlaut?"

"No, sir, not yet."

The President was attended by two trustees who, without bothering to be introduced, stated their views to him. "Very distinguished, Babcock tells me. Clever of Babcock to find him," one of them said. "Babcock is always looking out for the interests of the college," said the other, "even when he's abroad."

"His lectures will, I hope, be well attended." The President spoke with unwonted vagueness.

"Sure to be," said a trustee. "Babcock tells me his name is world-famous."

"Good," said the President, even more vaguely. "You must meet him, Hunter."

"Yes, sir. I'm looking forward to it."

"He's over there talking to Mr. Babcock now. You'll find, I'm sure, that he has some interesting ideas on American literature."

"Babcock tells me," said the other trustee eagerly, "that he has good ideas on everything. Sort of a universal man, Babcock says."

"Dean Pirbright, with whom he has been staying, has said something of the same sort to me." The President wagged his enormous head. "You can just go introduce yourself, Hunter. Babcock tells me that he doesn't insist on formality."

"Yes, sir." Nick moved toward the distinguished visitor, who he saw was occupied not only with a trustee, presumably Mr. Babcock, but with Sid Green. Nick felt no great impatience to present himself to Dr. Schlotlaut. He veered instead toward an adjacent group that contained Dean Pirbright, Dr. and Mrs. Purview, and Dr. Scroll, a young and saturnine medievalist.

"Have you met the latest benefaction of Mr. Babcock?" Dr. Scroll inquired. "Our newly purchased Nestor? Or better, perhaps, Aesculapius?" The medievalist spoke with bleak though erudite irony. His mockery reflected in somewhat more vigorous form what Nick had learned was the general faculty reaction to Dr. Schlotlaut's presence. Dr. Schlotlaut was resented, and it was clear that the little group here assembled was a nest of anti-Schlotlaut sentiments.

"Not Aesculapius, I think," Dean Pirbright said gravely. "There is nothing reptilian about him. Slimy perhaps, but not serpentine. More a bulldozer than a snake."

"I haven't met him," Nick said. "I hear he's very important."

"He is certainly that, by his own appraisal." Dr. Scroll unexpectedly smirked. "I have just left him. Of course

Pirbright has had him on his hands throughout the period of incognito. Very trying for him. We turned him over to young Green a moment ago. It would not be too much to say," Dr. Scroll added in an unpleasant voice, "that we have not so much left him as extricated ourselves from him. He clings."

"I insist less clinging than crushing," Dean Pirbright said obstinately.

"Anyway," said Nick, glancing toward the next group, "Sid's got away."

He was indeed approaching them, and in a manner that suggested a very tolerable precision in Dr. Scroll's phrase. He looked like someone who had extricated himself from something.

"Good God," Sid said upon arriving in their group.

"I told you you'd find it an experience." Dean Pirbright was suave. "A remarkable personality. I have had to cope with it for three weeks and you have had it for only three minutes. Half of the three weeks have been devoted to listening to the fruits of his researches into the private lives of Americans. I assure you that he has shown himself almost unbelievably skillful at this project. He has collected more repulsive gossip in three weeks than I hope anybody else could in three lifetimes. I don't know how good he is as a culture-sociologist, but he'd be a spectacular success as editor of *Dirt* magazine. The other half of the time has been spent arguing diplomatically about the titles of his lectures. The original titles he proposed were judged unsuitable by the higher authorities, but it has been extremely difficult to convince him of the soundness of their judgment."

"What did he want to call them?" asked Nick.

"There are, as you know, to be two lectures. The first was to be called 'Old Germandom and the Europe-Fate.' The second was to be called 'New Germandom and the

Europe-Fate.' Even Woodbine thought that these might discourage the most inveterate lecture-goers, so we had Sperry in the German Department put them back into German and then re-translate them into something more closely approximating English. Sperry ended up with 'German Culture and the Past of Europe,' and 'German Culture and the Future of Europe.' Not very sensational, but clear enough. Schlotlaut was furious. He agreed to accept them only when I told him that the announcements would have very large photographs of himself, so that nobody would really pay much attention to the titles of the lectures. They would know that anything Dr. Schlotlaut chose to speak on would be well worth their while. This worked perfectly. He is under the impression that his name is a household word even among the aborigines of Acropolis."

"He is also under the impression," Sid said irritably, "that he is an outstanding authority on chemistry. He has been kindly giving me some pointers on the latest developments in enzyme research. His colleague at Goofersburg, Herr Doktor Doktor von und zu Something-or-other, is the only sound man in the field. His work is going to revolutionize enzymes. It is truly 'destiny-pregnant,' Dr. Schlotlaut tells me."

"I think, Sid," Dean Pirbright said soothingly, "that he prefers to have his name pronounced in the German fashion, Shlut-lout, rather than Slot-lawt. The reason I think this is that he told me so. He is surprised and shocked by the lack of training in the principles of German pronunciation that he has found in America."

"One would suppose that he might prefer the Anglicization." Dr. Purview spoke broodingly. "The German form suggests so strongly the words 'slut' and 'lout.' But perhaps his vocabulary in English is not sufficiently extensive to include these words."

"Oh, yes, it is." Dean Pirbright was unaccustomedly

emphatic. "He has a very large English vocabulary. In fact he has a larger vocabulary than any native English-speaking person. He told me so. He mentioned it in the course of his explanation of why European schools are so excellent and American schools so miserably inadequate. 'The womb-place of illiteracy' is the phrase he chose to describe American schools. He believes that it is the superiority of European schools that accounts for the superiority of European culture in general."

"No," Dr. Scroll interrupted. "You are wrong. I will tell you. It is the weather."

Dean Pirbright looked doubtful. "The weather?"

"It is well known that the intellect cannot flourish except in the climate of Central Europe. It is this, he tells me, that accounts for the superiority of Germanic culture. It is not surprising, he further tells me, in view of the American climate, that American culture should be a vomit of undigested slops."

"Did he say *that?*" Sid Green positively recoiled.

"Well, to be perfectly accurate," Dr. Scroll went on briskly, "I think his words were 'an undigested slops-vomit.'"

"That sounds right," Dean Pirbright said. "He used a similar phrase to me on one occasion. It came up in the course of his explanation of why Americans are so lacking in tact, compared to, say, the Swiss. Tact, it has been found by one of his closest friends and colleagues, a world-famous scholar whose name, he tells me, I would not know, is the culture product of folk stability. Americans have, of course, no folk stability, and therefore no tact. Central Europeans, particularly members of Germandom, I gathered, are the only people who understand tact."

"Swine," Mrs. Purview said, loudly and pungently.

It was at this moment that Mr. Babcock led the distinguished visitor into their midst. They had approached from behind Mrs. Purview, and her expletive had been clearly audible. But Dr. Schlotlaut seemed not to have noticed anything. He was a florid, monolithic man with rimless glasses, and he was carrying a plate of *petit fours* from which he refreshed himself at intervals.

"Well," Mr. Babcock said, "I've brought the great man back to you professors. What he says is way over my head." He looked at Dr. Schlotlaut with admiration. "Have you met everybody, Doctor?"

"No." Dr. Schlotlaut conveyed with great clarity the impression that he did not want to meet everybody. A small but difficult pause ensued.

Professor Purview, who possessed a sort of dog-eared courtliness, stepped forward.

"My name is Purview," he said. "I don't believe we have met. I teach French. This is Mrs. Purview."

Dr. Schlotlaut, who had been looking out into space, turned and stared fixedly at the Purviews with an expression of shameless curiosity.

"And this," Dr. Purview went on, attempting to ignore the stare, "is Dr. Hunter of the English Department."

Dr. Schlotlaut was not interested in Dr. Hunter. He did not turn to look at him but continued his intensive scrutiny of the Purviews while taking another *petit four* from the plate and beginning to eat it. Nick thought that it might help to relieve the awkwardness and attract Dr. Schlotlaut's attention if he summoned up something from the German vocabulary he had accumulated as a military policeman in Munich. A comment in his own tongue might distract Dr. Schlotlaut, an end that was becoming more urgent each second. Mrs. Purview's face showed all too plainly that she disliked his examination.

"*Schmackhaft?*" Nick asked affably, alluding to the *petit fours*. Schlotlaut was indeed diverted. His features lit up. He spoke with his mouth full.

"Nein," he said. *"Es schmeckt nicht gut. Aber, Sie sprechen Deutsch?"*

Nick, his purpose accomplished, abandoned German. "Not much. A couple of words."

"But enough perhaps to understand the beauty of the language?" Dr. Schlotlaut regarded him benignly. "'*Schmackhaft!*' A beautiful word. A word for poets. Compare with it the French '*savoureux.*' A word forceless, beautyless. Or compare with it the English 'gustful.' What is gustful?"

"I don't know," Nick said.

"It is poetry-less." Dr. Schlotlaut selected another *petit four*. "It is only in German that true poetry can be written."

His audience received this in silence. Even Mr. Babcock seemed startled. "Shakespeare?" he asked tentatively.

"Hah," said Dr. Schlotlaut. "To find true beauty in Shakespeare's poetry you must read a German translation. I recommend you to Plötzgraben's translation. Plötzgraben is a great scholar and a great friend of mine. He is a true poet. He has also written the great critical work on Shakespeare." Dr. Schlotlaut munched appreciatively. *"Ein Blick Hinter die Kulissen der Shakespearepsychologie.* A work of indispensable importance for Shakespeare-understanding. And it also," he continued, growing careless about syntax in the heat of his enthusiasm for Plötzgraben, "most indispensable for the Anglo-Saxon psychology understanding is."

Anglo-Saxon psychology, as represented in the group that received this sentence, was for the moment paralyzed. Neither Mr. Babcock's fervor nor Dean Pirbright's suavities were capable of producing a comment upon Plötzgraben's work. The field was left unfortunately free for Mrs. Purview, who suffered from no Anglo-Saxon inhibitions.

"Tchah," she said distinctly, her gorgeous features distorted in a threatening frown.

While Dr. Schlotlaut was assimilating this remark, Mike

Kelly approached them, looking sullen as usual. He was not, Nick perceived, an addition who would do much to restore the conversational amenities nor to reduce the tensions that were rising like miasmic clouds around the little group.

"This German," Mrs. Purview said to him, "iss talking nonsense."

"I am not a German. I am a Swiss."

"You are no better than a German."

"May I present Dr. Kelly, of our French Department?" Dean Pirbright had judged it timely to repair this social omission.

Dr. Schlotlaut turned to Mike and subjected him to the same attitude of scrutiny with which he had a few minutes earlier studied the Purviews.

"*You* are Kelly," he said at length.

"Like all Germans, he talks nonsense," Mrs. Purview remarked, addressing Mike again.

"I do not talk nonsense. *Ever or ever,*" he turned on her.

Dr. Scroll was shaken out of the paralysis that had been creeping over the bystanders. "You are, I believe, engaged on some sort of research problem in Acropolis?"

It was the worst thing he could have said. Dr. Schlotlaut's complexion, never pale, was assuming a deep-eggplant shade.

"Yes." The monosyllable was spoken in tones sufficiently loud to attract attention from the surrounding guests. "Very important researches. Into depravity."

"*Ach, gut,*" Nick said in a futile diverting move.

"I have collected much information."

"Maybe you'd like another cup of punch," Mr. Babcock put in.

"No."

"They are all swine," Mrs. Purview observed, confidentially but audibly.

"My dear." Professor Purview spoke gently. "We have not yet had any refreshments. Shall we go have some punch? And some of those delicious little cakes?"

"And murderers," Mrs. Purview added.

This sentiment of hers, familiar to everyone who knew her, struck Dr. Schlotlaut with the force of novelty.

"I have discovered," he roared, "much about depravity in America. I have discovered that this crazy Lithuanian she-lady is having a sex life with this Kelly."

He spoke very loudly indeed, and he was undoubtedly heard by a considerable number of Mrs. Overton's guests. A still larger proportion of them were able to hear the forthcoming sentiments of Mrs. Purview.

"Swine," she screamed. "Murderer. Vermin."

A remarkably deep silence, spreading outward, ended the conversation in the rest of the room.

"Monster," Mrs. Purview cried.

Sid Green had put his hands on her shoulders and now he shook her brusquely. "Shut up," he said.

But Mrs. Purview had more to say, and no action of Sid's could prevent her saying it. Mike Kelly was regarding her with motionless horror. Elsa shook herself free from Sid's grip and hurled herself upon Dr. Schlotlaut.

"Of course I am. I love him because he is good and kind and not like Germans." Then she screamed again, a wordless, penetrating cry of concentrated hatred, and embedded her fingernails in Dr. Schlotlaut's cheeks.

It was, astonishingly, her husband who now sought to restrain her, and, more astonishingly still, with success. His sagging face was as colorless as Dr. Schlotlaut's was puce, and his expression was one of unutterable distress. But he took her arm with remarkable firmness and pulled her off. He even managed to murmur hoarsely but imperatively the necessary words.

"We shall go now, Elsa," he said.

And she went, following him limply.

"This Lithuanian she-bitch is crazy," Dr. Schlotlaut observed, his handkerchief to his face.

Around them the flow of conversation resumed, like the coming of the first autumn raindrops on an arid field, dripping tentatively, coursing in uncertain rivulets, then beating down in a determined effort to drown the horrid interruption of Mrs. Overton's reception. Mike Kelly slid toward the door. In his absence, the reception went on.

Chapter XIII   Comprehensive Examination

*T*he distressing events at the President's reception had the effect upon Parthenon College of those electrical disturbances of the atmosphere that cause dental fillings to transmit radio programs. Dr. Schlotlaut's revelations, whose subject had for some months hovered inaudibly on the conversational airwaves of Acropolis, were now heard in full volume in varied milieux. There was no one among the several score guests at the President's house who had not listened to the interchange between the eminent visitor and Mrs. Purview, and immediately afterward the subject began to crackle like persistent static on a hundred different wave lengths.

Official cognizance was taken the next morning in the President's office. Closeted with the Dean of the Faculty and the Provost, Dr. Overton explored its ramifications, as numerous as they were painful.

"The public reaction has been, as one would expect,

strenuous," he observed. "Sympathies appear to be divided, although by no means evenly. I have had eight demands from divers persons, led by Mr. Babcock, that Kelly be dismissed immediately. There have been six persons who urged the banishment of Dr. Schlotlaut and the cancellation of his lectures. Four have demanded both. And there have been three, all of them women, requiring that something be done about Mrs. Purview."

"I should have thought *that* was Dr. Purview's problem, not ours." Dean Pirbright sounded anxious to divest himself of at least one ramification.

"Undoubtedly," the President said. "We cannot, after all, deport a faculty member's wife against the wishes of the faculty member. Of course, we don't know what his wishes are. But I told the ladies that the Purviews' affairs were no concern of the college. Which is, of course, not true."

"No," the Provost said sadly. He was a fastidious man who looked like a slightly wizened judge, and he spoke with great precision. "It could scarcely be further from the truth. In a—ah—procedural sense, however, you were certainly correct."

"Good." The President nodded heavily. "That's one thing settled. I have also had some other communications relating to the affair which I suppose we may disregard. One was made of letters cut out of newspapers. It accused me of being a whoremonger. Its writer must have worked very quickly indeed. It was mailed at nine-thirty last night."

"Ah," said Dean Pirbright.

"There have also been two telephone calls, which Marian took, from anonymous persons who believe that this incident demonstrates definitely that the College is dominated by Reds."

There was a pause. "I think," the Provost said judicially, "that we may disregard them, as—ah—tangential."

"Good. The questions remaining are, what we do about Schlotlaut and what we do about Kelly."

Dean Pirbright considered. When he spoke, it was in an almost expressionless voice. "I have given the matter of Schlotlaut my closest attention in the last twelve hours. Much as I should like to extract his fingernails slowly with hot pincers, I have concluded that it would be wiser to do nothing at all. He had better give the lectures and leave immediately afterward. Anything else would attract comment."

"Anything at all will attract comment," the President said. He shook himself with the motion of an unhappy hippopotamus wallowing morosely in muddy water. "But I agree. It will attract *least* attention if we allow him to go ahead. Moreover, Babcock remains wedded to him. I think he must have hypnotized Babcock."

The Provost, looking more judicial and more fastidious than ever, spoke in a slightly reproachful manner, shaking his head. "It is a possible hypothesis that Schlotlaut is the sort of man who gives the semi-literate the impression of basking in reflected culture. The shallow calling to the shallow. They feel it only appropriate if he's—ah—revolting, since they feel subconsciously that culture is revolting. I agree, however. There's nothing to do but let him give his—ah—revolting lectures and disseminate further among the semi-literate the gratifying sensation of touching bottom in a sea of profundity."

"Good. Now. Kelly."

"*Kelly!*" Dean Pirbright spoke as if some dangerous chemical reaction had been rashly introduced into the conversation for the first time. "Babcock is very insistent that he must go, and so are some of the other trustees. We shall have to take steps. They are worrying about the good name of the college."

"I am sure they are," Dean Pirbright said. "They always do."

"As I see it, the best thing from the point of view of the good name of the college, and our own convenience as well, would be to follow the usual procedure in cases of moral turpitude among faculty members. There have, fortunately, been no such cases for some years now, but I have looked up the usual procedure. I see no alternative."

"And what is the usual procedure?"

"A joint *ad hoc* committee."

"Of course," Dean Pirbright said. "What else?"

"Consisting," the President went on, "of two board members, four members of the faculty, representing each rank, and ourselves *ex officio*."

"And what does this committee do to the *hoc?*"

"It considers it," the President said weightily. "It hears a statement by the offender. It then reaches a decision. *In rem*. I had thought of Dr. Goodge. To lend dignity."

The Dean nodded.

"And Professor Obdyke, as a suitable Associate. And for the Assistant, Gregory, whom I judge to be timid and not likely to cause trouble. For the instructor, I thought of Hunter. He is a laconic young man. Someone who doesn't talk much is indicated. Do you regard Hunter as—ah—sufficiently"—the President appeared to grope for suitable terms—"reliable?"

"I think he's reliable enough," Dean Pirbright said.

"Good. I shall send out notices at once. The sooner we inter all this, the better. Not that the interment will be final. The corpse will stir in its grave for years to come. Just to mention one thing, I doubt if my wife will ever bring herself to give another reception."

The Dean and Provost nodded again and clucked sympathetically, although the effect of these expressions of condolence was somewhat weakened when they caught one another's eyes and grinned.

"And now perhaps we had best engage in a little advance planning for the *ad hoc* committee."

The Dean and the Provost nodded. They settled themselves in their chairs for a little advance planning.

At their breakfast table Professor and Mrs. Nutter renewed a conversation which had agreeably occupied them from the previous afternoon until past their usual bedtime.

"I slept badly," Mrs. Nutter said, consuming a piece of whole wheat toast.

"Did you, Lambie?"

"Yes. Worrying about poor old Purview."

"A maniac, Puss. No need to worry."

"Don't talk nonsense. Who?"

"Purview. A native of Maine. They're notoriously tough."

"The humiliation will kill him."

"No it won't."

Mrs. Nutter chewed in silence for a moment. "Of course, it's not as bad as it would have been if things had been different."

"Different?"

"I happen to know that they were married in name only."

"Do you, Cherry-Pooh? And how do you happen to know that?"

"But it doesn't excuse her, of course," Mrs. Nutter continued. "Or *him*."

Professor Nutter chuckled. The course of the conversation seemed to fill him with satisfaction. More than ever he resembled a well-fed bird. "You're right there, dearie. It certainly doesn't excuse him. Purview thought so well of him, too. Very sound on Corneille. He said so just the other day. Well, sound on Corneille, unsound on everything else."

He chuckled again, and poured himself coffee. "Very few department chairmen are good judges of character. I could have told Purview from the beginning that the boy was unreliable."

"Unreliable!" Mrs. Nutter fairly spat the word. "A libertine. Disgusting." She selected a second piece of toast and bit into it with zest. "Unreliable!" She appeared to find her husband guilty of understatement so extreme as to be morally reprehensible. "Fool," she added, rounding off her appraisal of the situation.

If the conversation of the President and the Deans was businesslike and that of the Nutters gay in their own unusual fashion, another interview that day was frankly grim. Brandon Craig telephoned Nick at eight o'clock and arranged to meet him for lunch at Acropolis Eats.

He arrived a little late, and as he came toward the booth Nick was struck by the effect that Mike's difficulties seemed to have had on Craig. It was clear that he had not slept much. His face was white and lined and he was limping more than usual.

"Christ," he said, sitting down.

"What's likely to happen?" Nick asked. "I tried to get hold of him this morning, but nobody answered either the doorbell or the telephone."

"So did I." Craig was hopeless. "He's there, all right. But he won't see anybody. They'll can him, of course."

"They will, eh." Nick was reflective rather than inquiring.

"Of course. There's nothing else for them to do. Especially with Babcock on their heels. He's a great one for high-mindedness. And of course Overton is, too. Not that he believes in it himself, I imagine. But he'll put on a show to please the public. That's his specialty."

Nick said nothing.

"What's maddening," Craig went on, "is that they didn't

give a damn what went on as long as it was kept quiet.
But now it's public, they'll get dressed up in long white
robes and wring their hands. They'll talk about the traditions of Parthenon and its mission of character-building.
They're like the worst kind of politicians. All campaign
promises and baby-kissing. Worse than politicians," he
added with irrelevant venom. "Mike's a fool."

"I suppose he is."

"I've been telling him so for a year. Repeatedly in the
last two weeks, since we had that talk, you and Sid and I.
He wouldn't break it off, though. That doesn't necessarily
make him a fool, but for a long time he was convinced that
nobody knew about it, although everybody in town was
gossiping. Then a few weeks ago he began to wake up.
That's what's so damnable ironic. He'd heard people were
talking. He was going to make Elsa break it off until things
got straightened out."

"Straightened out?"

"He thought he could get her to divorce old Purview
and they could get married. What he wants to marry her
for, I don't know. Or rather, I do know. Anybody who
looked at her could understand all too clearly. But she's
practically imbecilic. He was a fool about that too, because
he could never stay here in Purview's department if he'd
broken up his marriage and then married the bitch. But he
thought he could talk everybody into it. In his good moods
he always expects everybody to be rational. If there's one
thing academic people aren't, it's rational. They're in business, like everybody else, so they've got to please the
customers."

"What do they do now?"

"I hear from Sid, who heard from Obdyke, that they'll
have a trial. Ostensibly. Actually less a trial than an au-
topsy. They'll call Mike in and hear what he has to say

and then fire him. They have an *ad hoc* committee. Trustees, administration, faculty."

Nick started violently. "A what?"

"An *ad hoc* committee."

"I'll be damned," Nick said. "Is that what it is?"

For the first time in the course of this gloomy conversation, Brandon showed some of his usual animation. "What what is?"

"I'm on the damned thing. I got a notice from the President just before I came over. It didn't say what we were supposed to do, so I didn't know what it was." He paused, contemplating the possibilities of the situation. "Maybe I can do some good."

Brandon shook his head bleakly. "No, you can't. I can see what happened. They put you on because they have to have an instructor, and they thought you'd cause less trouble because of being new and presumably scared about your own job. But even if you tried something, they'd outvote you eight to one. The President and the Provost, the Dean, and two trustees. Even if the faculty members all voted together, which they won't, you'd still be outvoted. So it wouldn't do any good to try. So for God's sake, don't try. There's no point in getting yourself a reputation as a dissolute Bolshevik just to satisfy your own bloody loyalty. In the long run they'd probably decide that you didn't fit into the Parthenon Family, and they'd terminate your appointment."

"I'm not sure I'd mind having my appointment terminated. Under the circumstances."

"Don't be a sentimental fool, Stu. It wouldn't be any better anywhere else. And you've got to have a job. Scholars have to eat."

So fierce were Brandon's tones that they recalled to Nick his evening at Muse Street months before, and Dean Scarlett's observation that Craig was a dedicated scholar. Nick looked at him appraisingly. Nothing about his present state seemed dedicated.

"Sure." Nick moved the salt and pepper shakers into more symmetrical positions about the sugar bowl, considering the contradictions in Brandon's character. "But since the academic profession is so damned corrupt, why bother about it? Why not be just as corrupt in some other line, where it pays better?"

Brandon looked up in surprise. "Well, there's no other kind of job where you have the time to do your own work."

"Your own work?"

"I'm working on a book on seventeenth-century legal philosophy. If I wasn't teaching, I wouldn't have a chance to finish it." He paused and looked down, frowning, as if he had somehow committed an indiscretion. "Anyway," he added, "before you go voting against the official position in that committee, Stu, you'd better consider whether you'd rather have two weeks' vacation or three months. Before you take a high moral stand, think about those vacations."

He took up a menu and bleakly studied it. "Nauseous stuff they give you to eat here," he said.

The Joint *Ad Hoc* Committee assembled in the Kriedler Memorial Room, which had been built in honor, and with the bequest, of a Utica bibliophile named Adam G. Kriedler, of the Class of 1854. Mr. Kriedler had left the money to provide a repository for his extensive library of works by anti-Darwinian philosophers. His Memorial Room was large and lofty, but like many other rooms at Parthenon it was now somewhat decayed, and inadequately lit by slitlike lancets filled with deplorable stained glass.

The present committee, gathered in the perpetual Gothic dusk, was depressed by the surroundings into a state of whispering solemnity. Even the President seemed inclined to moderate his speaking voice. The rest of the committee

was inclined to total silence. It was difficult to make out
very clearly the forms and faces of the individual members.
The shadowy figures silently seated themselves around the
large oaken refectory table.

These proceedings Nick observed with a discomfort and
a dislike verging upon desperation. He had a strong impulse, during the period of silent prayer, to break into a
loud rendering of some very ribald song. The comportment
of the committee, very exactly matching the fraudulent
and lugubrious décor of the Memorial Room, bore out
Brandon Craig's diagnosis of its intentions. It was preparing
to butcher Mike Kelly to make an academic holiday.

"Good," the President said at last.

The committee looked at him expectantly, and some of
them took up the pencils which lay with an accompanying
tablet before each member.

"Well." He paused impressively. "We have the unfortunate duty of examining an alleged case of misconduct of
a rather serious nature on the part of a junior member of
this faculty who, in accordance with the regulations of the
college and the ancient principles of justice and the common law which are our cherished heritage"—here, Dr. Overton raised his eyes to the groined vaulting above him—
"will now be permitted to present himself and his case
before this Joint *Ad Hoc* Committee of his—ah—peers." It
was evident that there was some doubt in his mind as to
whether all the members of the committee could properly
be described as peers. "His peers, and others," the President amended.

"Dr. Kelly is waiting outside. Before we ask him to come
in, I shall review briefly the facts of the case. If I err in
any matter of detail, or if I appear to those of you who are
also acquainted with the background to be doing any injustice in my presentation, any one of you must feel entirely
free to interrupt." He looked around the room. It appeared

likely from the frozen faces of the committee members that his words had failed to incite any great feeling of freedom to interrupt.

He reviewed briefly the facts of the case. His brevity was indeed so marked as to seem deadly. The extreme succinctness of his summary suggested that the details were of no interest or concern to the committee.

"And now," he concluded, "we shall ask Dr. Kelly to come in. Unless there are any questions?"

There were no questions. Dr. Kelly was summoned.

Even in that shadowy room his pallor was noticeable as he entered, and so was an unfortunate aggressiveness of manner. His shoulders were squared, his chin protruded, his eyes blazed with sullen fury. It was clear that Dr. Kelly, far from being contrite, was determined to be provocative.

"Sit down, Dr. Kelly," the President said with unexpected cordiality.

"I'll stand up," Mike said. He took a position at the end of the table with his legs apart and his hands on the back of an empty chair.

"Now, Dr. Kelly," the President continued in his affable manner, "we are sorry to have to bring you here on a matter which I assure you is as distressing to us as to you. But in all fairness"—Mike uttered a sound, small but disagreeable—"we wish to hear anything you may have to say."

"I don't have anything to say."

"You are, of course, aware of the situation that has arisen," the President went on, as if he had failed to hear Mike's sentence, "and of the gravamen of the charges of moral turpitude. . . ." His voice trailed off. His head fell in a jerky series of movements, as if it were descending a steep staircase, onto his chest. He breathed heavily. The President had gone to sleep.

There was an appalling pause. Mike Kelly turned still

whiter. One of the trustees twisted his pencil compulsively in his fingers. The faculty members stared into the dusky reaches of the vaulting. The pause prolonged itself. Dr. Obdyke, who was inclined to impatience, shook himself and coughed.

". . . which have been inescapably brought to the attention of a lamentably large section of . . ." The President's nap had apparently extinguished his cordiality. He appeared drowsily uncertain as to just what it was that a large section of had had brought to its attention, and after staring fixedly for several seconds at Mike Kelly he abandoned the sentence. "We naturally wish to give you every opportunity to . . ." Once again he broke off, unable to state just what sort of opportunity he wished to give, and it looked for a moment as if he might go to sleep again. "We wish, in short, to hear anything you may want to say."

"I don't want to say anything."

"Good. That is to say, are you sure?"

"Yes."

The President appeared for once in his life baffled. Mike's recalcitrance was clearly unexpected. "Good," he said again, but rather tentatively, and looked around at the committee. "In that case . . ."

Mike remained stonily motionless. The President shifted in his chair. The committee looked at the table. Nick had averted his glance from Mike after his first appearance. However the situation appeared to others, to Mike his presence must seem an unfriendly act and, worse, a guilty association with the forces of law, order, and hypocrisy. To himself, his presence appeared in a still more unfavorable light. His own misdeeds were on a scale so vast as to constitute not only an affront but an actual crime against Mike Kelly. He was not only associating himself with allies in hypocrisy; he was associating himself with

them under circumstances so monumentally false as to
baffle all conscience and all reason. His earlier impulse to
sing ribald songs was now replaced by a vision of himself
rising to make a full confession. In the confusion that
would follow such an act, he dreamily considered, the case
of Mike Kelly would disappear into innocuous triviality.
The moral postures of the *ad hoc* committee would be
fractured irrevocably. It was not beyond possibility that a
full confession would prevent any future *ad hoc* committee
from ever meeting. In one moment Nick would recover
(or, more accurately, achieve) his independence and his
integrity, and free himself from a situation not only embarrassing but evil.

These daydreams were interrupted by the President's
voice. ". . . in that case, we need not detain you further."

Mike surveyed the table with venomous antipathy and
withdrew.

Nick glanced at his colleagues. They looked as grim as
they did uncomfortable. There could be no doubt as to
Mike's fate.

Nor was this, objectively considered, surprising. It was
difficult to imagine a worse witness than Mike Kelly. His
attitude had conveyed not only antipathy but an emphatic
invitation to retribution. He had been beyond question
asking for trouble, from a motive that appeared disagreeably close to contempt.

The President was staring down the table at the empty
chair as if Mike were still standing behind it. His large
eyes had narrowed to a meditative slit; he gave the impression of a president still mentally framing difficult questions for the defendent, or perhaps wrestling with some
abstruse problem of Latin syntax. There was nothing in his
rather inscrutable expression that suggested forgiveness.
Beside him old Dr. Goodge sat perfectly rigid. His thin
and rocklike features under his translucent skin composed

a picture of total austerity. Nor, to judge from his expression, was Dr. Obdyke of more yielding inclination. Despite the roseate chubbiness of his face and his jaunty bow tie his eyes were motionless and steely. Next to him young Gregory's expression conveyed nothing but embarrassment and, Nick thought, timidity in the presence of so large a concentration of dignity and authority. The two trustees also appeared embarrassed, although not intimidated. Their faces were a good deal blander than those of their academic colleagues, and Mr. Babcock wore the somewhat set look of vacant cordiality that is commonly encountered in elevators. Mr. Trexler appeared resolutely affable. Neither of them looked like men who were prepared to countenance a public scandal. Only the Dean and the Provost showed the slightest sign of relaxation. Both of them were wearing the adumbration of a smile, but in both cases a bleak, sardonic smile.

The first movement came from Mr. Trexler. He took a pack of cigarettes from his pocket, lit one, coughed slightly, and shook himself in a motion of decorous sadness, as if the patient had finally breathed his last, so permitting some small opportunity for relaxation.

"Good!" The President ended the silence with his customary expletive. "We must now proceed to the unpleasant business of considering our decision upon this most regrettable affair." He paused. "I may say, speaking as president, that the legal position is perfectly clear. Dr. Kelly's appointment was for a term of two years and would normally run for the remainder of the present academic year and for one more thereafter. But the grounds for terminating such an appointment are clearly stated in the Faculty Regulations and are of a sort that is usual if not universal in colleges and universities. I have assured myself that Dr. Kelly is familiar with these regulations. He knows that appointments may be terminated at any time

in cases of . . ." The President's commanding oratory had
been simmering down to *piano* for the last few clauses.
Now it ceased altogether, and he began to snore lightly.

The death watch resumed.

". . . moral turpitude. *At any time.*" His volume restored
fully, the President appeared to be addressing the empty
chair in tones of strong reproach. "You have heard Dr.
Kelly. There is, I take it, no substantial difference of opinion about the facts of the matter. I may say—speaking as
priest as well as president—that there would seem to be
three considerations to be borne in mind in arriving at our
decision. *First*"—he paused and looked around the room—
"there can be no question whatever concerning Dr. Kelly's
scholarly and professional qualifications—even his considerable intellectual distinction. Dr. Purview himself—most
justly and generously—has given me ample assurances on
that point. Secondly, there can be no question but that acts
of a most distressing nature"—he seemed to grope for the
mot juste—"of a lamentably *overt* nature as well, have taken
place. Third, however much we may sympathize with any
individual or individuals concerned, we must of course
regard our obligation to the College as transcendent." His
voice had risen to an emotive roar with this stirring climax.
But his call to duty did not seem to evoke any enthusiasm
from the other members of the Committee. They regarded
him stolidly in their former attitudes.

Mike's coffin, Nick thought, was now being assembled.
The hammering in of its nails would commence in a moment.

"It is our custom in committees of this sort," the President
went on, "to call upon members in order of seniority. The
representatives of the Board of Trustees, as members of
the governing body of this college, will therefore speak
first. Mr. Babcock?"

Mr. Babcock took off his spectacles, laid them deliberately upon the table, removed a handkerchief from his pocket with the evident intention of polishing them, thought better of it, replaced both spectacles and handkerchief, and stared down the table. He looked like a man who was trying to strike the right note in an unfamiliar environment and had concluded, without much conviction, that high-mindedness combined with solemn amiability was proper.

"Nasty business," he said at last. "First time anything like this has happened since I've been on the board. I don't like it."

"I'm sure we shall all agree with you on that point," the President remarked.

"As you say, Overton, we must think of the reputation of the college. If it had been kept quiet"—Mr. Babcock revealed a certain hesitation, evidently aware that he was treading on rather peculiar moral ground but convinced that firm terrain lay somewhere ahead in this general direction—"that is to say, if it were not for the overtness, as you so illuminatingly put it, Overton—" He broke off again. "We can't risk scandals. We must think of the parents' reactions. They wouldn't want their boys being taught by somebody like that. I'm not sure I'd want my own boy taught by him."

"That," the President said judiciously, "is of course a consideration."

Mr. Babcock appeared encouraged. "So he'll have to be fired. Nothing else to do."

"Mr. Trexler?"

Mr. Trexler, though as uncomfortable as Mr. Babcock, appeared much surer about what the situation called for. He adopted an attitude of rueful bonhomie.

"Well, well," Mr. Trexler said cheerfully, "it's all too bad. I suppose he won't be able to get another job?"

"He would certainly be handicapped in looking for one

if he were dismissed from Parthenon," said the President.

"Well, probably better if he doesn't. Dangerous man to have around."

"Dr. Goodge?"

The professor of theology, the venerable authority on webfeet and coyotes, rose formally. It was the first time anybody had risen, and the effect was to make all previous speakers seem reprehensibly casual, even flippant. Dr. Goodge's stately person and bearing increased this effect. He was very impressive and very venerable, and he spoke in a deep and measured bass, each consonant emerging like the tolling of some ancient bell.

"You say"—he addressed the President—"that you speak as priest as well as president. I should hope that this will signify that, as priest, you are as fully aware of the ubiquity of fleshly temptations as you are prepared to absolve those who, having yielded to them, have duly confessed their sin. I should hope that it will signify that, as president, you would cherish above all else the achievements of the human mind and the rare and precious attainments of true scholarship."

Dr. Goodge cleared his throat portentously. Nick listlessly sank deeper into his chair. If they were going to can Mike, the quicker they did so the better. He found Dr. Goodge tiresome. The entire proceedings were as dull as they were distasteful.

"The good name of this institution," Dr. Goodge continued liturgically, "depends, as must the good name of any institution of education, upon one thing and one thing alone. It depends upon the intellectual attainments and scholarly distinction of its members. There can be no doubt that in these respects Dr. Kelly is outstanding. It would therefore appear to be a crime, and worse than a crime a blunder, and worse than a blunder a sin, to consider his dismissal. I must aver in the strongest possible terms that

I favor the honoring of his contract and the continuance of his membership in this faculty."

Nick sat up.

The President was immobile and inscrutable. Mr. Trexler opened and closed his mouth mutely. Mr. Babcock removed his spectacles, laid them upon the table, and replaced them.

"Dr. Obdyke?" The President was noncommittal.

Dr. Obdyke also rose. He was shorter, rounder, and younger than Dr. Goodge. But although he spoke in a staccato patter he was not without a certain peppery dignity of his own.

"Well, sir, it's all most unfortunate, most. But we mustn't confuse public relations with true reputation, must we? Nor private morals with academic morals. Young Kelly appears to be a fool as regards all practical considerations, but our demands on him are fortunately not of a practical nature. This is not a girls' school. We do not guarantee the purity of our faculty, any more than we demand purity from our undergraduates as a requirement for the bachelor's degree. It is not," he said with unexpected ferocity, staring at Mr. Trexler, "as if young Kelly had falsified a footnote."

"Had done *what?*" Mr. Trexler, having disastrously misjudged the climate of opinion, was baffled and vexed.

"If a soldier betrays to the enemy," Dr. Obdyke continued more equably, as if explaining a difficult point in biochemistry to a freshman, "he is shot. We should be obliged to shoot young Kelly if he had betrayed us—plagiarized, for example, or mistranslated deliberately, or something really serious of that sort. But if a soldier spends a night with a prostitute, he is not shot. He is not court-martialed." He resumed an expression of great malevolence as he stared at Mr. Trexler. "He is not even rebuked."

"I don't know what you're talking about," Mr. Trexler said.

"No." Dr. Obdyke was cheerful again. "I don't suppose you do."

"And now the Provost." The President spoke rather quickly.

"Well, I'm not sure I'd go quite so far as Dr. Goodge and Dr. Obdyke." The Provost, his small, finely formed features wholly impassive, glanced around the room with the air of one impregnably impartial. "There are certain possible defects of judgment and private morals that would to my mind impair a teacher's usefulness, to the point perhaps of negating his—ah—scholarly integrity." He paused while his colleagues roved among the more distressing possibilities in the realm of defective private morals. "I think for example of an old professor of my own. It was his eccentricity to go without an overcoat, even in the coldest weather. As a consequence he was afflicted with chronic laryngitis, so that upon occasion his lectures were incomprehensible. Happily, Dr. Kelly's lapses are not of so serious a character."

"I think it's damned serious," Mr. Trexler said.

"Of course, serious enough," the Provost agreed. "I only meant that from our point of view Mr. Kelly's defects of judgment are not related to his calling, as were those of my old professor. In Kelly's case his professional qualifications are not in any way affected. But of *course*, serious enough, in a different sphere. A sphere which is not the concern of this committee."

"But you heard the President," Mr. Babcock said a little plaintively. "Overton said that moral turpitude was our concern."

"If I may speak for the President—" Dean Pirbright now interrupted. His manner was smooth and insinuating. "Speaking as the Dean of the Faculty, in which capacity

I have a particular concern for the Faculty Regulations, I may say that questions of moral turpitude are to be construed as falling within the realm of this committee *if* the committee feels that the particular instance offers grounds for considering the termination of an appointment. If the committee does *not* feel that the case in question offers such grounds, as Dr. Goodge and Dr. Obdyke and the Provost do not, of course we have no concern with moral turpitude *qua* moral turpitude. I might add that my own judgment coincides with that of Dr. Goodge, Dr. Obdyke, and the Provost."

Confronted with this intricate syllogism Mr. Babcock looked numb.

"Dr. Gregory?"

"Oh," Dr. Gregory squirmed. "I agree with them."

"You agree with whom?" the President asked politely.

"I think that if a man's a good teacher and a good scholar, we ought to keep him."

The meeting was moving rapidly. It was like a roller coaster which having mounted creakily to the peak of its artificial mountain was now proceeding downward at increasing velocity. Nick found its progress too rapid for full comprehension. He was aware only of surprise and of a complicated sense of awe.

"Dr. Hunter?"

"I agree with Gregory, sir."

"Six to two," the President observed with finality.

"But look here," Mr. Trexler said. It was he rather than Mr. Babcock whose independence of judgment had survived the crushing weight of six faculty members. "This is all very well. I don't know what Mr. Obdyke means when he says that public relations and reputation aren't the same thing—in my business they are. But even if they aren't you've got to admit that public relations matter, and what we're doing is damned bad public relations."

"May I ask in what way?" Dr. Obdyke spoke icily.

"What Babcock said earlier, for one thing. Parents will probably hear about all this, and when they do they won't want their boys to come here. We'll get a bad name, and we can't afford that. No organization can afford that. A college is like a business, after all. You've got to keep up your name for quality."

"But not quality itself?" Dean Pirbright, the sophist, moved rapidly into Mr. Trexler's logical breech.

"Eh?"

"You don't think it matters what the quality of our product is, merely what people think it is?"

"Of course I care about its quality. That's what bothers me. We're selling damaged goods here, in the form of this Kelly, and what's more, the customers are going to find out they're damaged."

"But what are the goods we're selling?"

"Decent conduct of course."

"But, as Dr. Obdyke remarked, we don't guarantee the purity of our faculty any more than we demand purity from undergraduates as a requirement for graduation. Propriety is not listed among the offerings in our catalogue. There is no course in Propriety I, nor any in Advanced Propriety, nor any seminar in Selected Problems of Propriety. We are not selling propriety of conduct, Mr. Trexler." Dean Pirbright's aloof, ingratiating deference had not changed, but he spoke with resolution.

"Well, not primarily, maybe." Mr. Trexler was dogged as well as dismayed. "But it's something the customers have the right to expect. An implied warranty, as we say in my line of business. Speaking as a parent, I'd say they have a duty to their boys to expect it."

"You feel," the Provost said a little dreamily, as if lost in faraway speculations on the nature of goodness, "that the boys are likely to be—ah—corrupted by Dr. Kelly?"

"Well, you might put it that way."

"May I ask"—his tones were still meditative, and rather wistful—"what fraternity you belonged to?"

"I don't see what that has to do with it."

"Oh, merely that I have the impression that you were a Zeta. If you've kept in touch with your House you may know that—"

"This has nothing to do with it."

The Provost's pale eyes were staring into remote, celestial spheres. His voice came like a trail of pipe smoke. "If I were Dr. Kelly's father, I think that I might worry quite a lot about his being—ah—corrupted by contact with the Zetas. If I were a very strict father I don't know that I should want my son to teach here at all."

"That's a hell of a thing to say about Parthenon."

"Or," the Provost continued delicately, as if approaching an unwonted but unavoidable coarseness, "at Yale or Princeton. Or even Bryn Mawr."

"That's not the point," Mr. Trexler said, adopting another one. "The point is what people think. Parents and headmasters."

Dr. Goodge cleared his throat. In the tense atmosphere of the Kriedler Room it sounded like the first clap of a distant thunderstorm.

"The problem you discern then, Mr. Trexler, is limited to the *scandal* concerning the indiscretions of Dr. Kelly and—a point of coeval importance which we have hitherto disregarded—of Mrs. Purview? Had the sin been, as it were, a discretion instead of an indiscretion, no difficulty would have arisen in your mind? You would not have been concerned about the corrupting influence of a faculty member, and a faculty member's wife, upon the decency of the students' morals?"

"If the students and their parents didn't know it, it wouldn't hurt them." Mr. Trexler had spoken hastily. He now perceived the pitfalls of his position. "But that's not what I mean. What I mean is— Oh, hell!"

"I fancied that's what you meant," Dr. Goodge said.

President Overton spoke in a conciliatory tone. "The scandal must not be exaggerated. I take it that Dr. Goodge used the word in a theological rather than a colloquial sense. The indiscretion was overt—or at least it was overtly revealed—but it wasn't very public. It has not been in the newspapers. Unlike, I am sorry to say, the more massive indiscretions of the Zetas. We may assume, I think, that it will prove to be a seven-days' wonder. Perhaps we may be guided by the memory of that unfortunate episode of old Miss Prendergast and the exchange student from Iraq. You will recall that despite its somewhat sensational aspect a week served to obliterate almost all traces of that little catastrophe. No doubt the present problem will fade away with comparable celerity, provided of course"—and here the President looked at Mr. Trexler with an attitude of formidable determination—"that it does not get into the newspapers. Which it won't unless this committee should vote to dismiss Dr. Kelly. And that we have just voted six to two against."

So magistral was the President's delivery, so adamantine his posture, that even Mr. Trexler could not avoid the conclusion that the meeting was terminated. With only a moment's pause he rose.

"Well," he said without evident rancor, "I guess I'll have to be getting along."

The President also rose and smiled warmly.

"I hope that you and Mrs. Trexler will be able to stop long enough to join Mrs. Overton and myself in a little refreshment at my house before you go on?"

"I've got—I've got to get away."

The President held out his hand.

"Good! That is to say, a pity," he said heartily.

Nick walked back across the campus with Dean Pirbright, who had shown a tenacious disposition to accompany him. He did not entirely welcome this company—he was not in a state of mind to welcome any company. The committee meeting had had upon him the effect of a psychic concussion, inducing a vision of stars and skyrockets. Further, these celestial lights had appeared to him in the form of a pattern, and they illuminated larger patterns whose details he wanted to work out alone. The whole of Parthenon had begun to take on an awesome symmetry, and even the bare branches overhead contributed to the subtle intricacy of the composition. It was as if a painting of elevated moral and aesthetic qualities had hung before him concealed by a sheet. During the last six months, corners of the sheet had been lifted, and now it had been torn away, and the painting brightly lit by the shooting stars.

Courtesy, however, obliged him to walk with Dean Pirbright, and to attend to his conversation.

"Tiresome," the Dean said. "Such meetings are very wearing morally. One is left with a lingering sympathy for the opposition. I'm afraid we rather manhandled them. Especially poor Babcock. He has no staying power."

"He asked for it."

"Doubtless. But he didn't know he was asking for it. However, by the same token I suppose that he didn't know he was being manhandled." Dean Pirbright laughed dryly. "I'm sorry that Scarlett couldn't have been there. He would have enjoyed the performance. And he would have been useful. He has a very deft touch with trustees."

Nick did not answer.

"I suppose," Dean Pirbright went on musingly, "we *were* a trifle unfair in not meeting Babcock on his own terms. It was like using atom bombs in a fencing match. The President was worried beforehand that our guns might be too big and blast Babcock into insensibility before he had time to surrender. But in their different ways, both Obdyke and the Provost are by way of being experts at logical small arms."

"Beforehand? Was this all . . . ?"

"No. Not in any detail. We knew we could count on the academic mind to shoot from the hip by reflex, if I may mix an anatomical metaphor. The President had a talk with the Provost and myself, but it was not in any complete sense a strategy conference. And we should not have dared to speak to Goodge or Obdyke—or Gregory or yourself. You would all have regarded it quite rightly as interference. But we were naturally able to guess what your reactions would be—what any scholar's reactions would be."

Nick trusted himself with nothing more than a nod.

"Of course, one could not expect Babcock—or Trexler either—to understand our position, which was why it was necessary to outwit him rather than simply outargue him. He is out of his depth among educated people. That's not his fault or even I suppose his misfortune, in the ordinary way of things. He's made quite a lot of money, which he probably couldn't have done if he had been educated. To be a success in business, Stuart, it is necessary to accept hazy absolutes, such as 'It is a positive good for the world to consume more Superdupes,' or 'A successful Superdupe executive is by definition the model of what a man ought to be.' I don't belittle all this—the world needs absolutes, even hazy ones. But you and I and other educated men couldn't accept them. Our profession is to dissect assumptions. We must question Superdupes, just as Babcock must accept absolutes. I am sure he is capable of believing as many as six impossible things before breakfast, like the White Queen."

"And you don't think that we—that is, academic people —believe impossible things?"

"Only after we have discovered that they are impossible, and then with caution. We know our principles to be pragmatically sound, and we believe them to be morally sound as well. But we are always examining them. The thing that made today's meeting so exhausting was that, as everyone thoughtfully pointed out to them, neither Trexler nor Babcock has the faintest notion what our professional principles are. We believe that intellectual values count, and we don't, professionally speaking, care about anything else. Trexler and Babcock have an absolute for any situation—usually several—and care passionately about them. Being uneducated, they cannot understand what we mean by education."

Dean Pirbright paused. If it were possible for so assured a man to feel embarrassment, it might have been supposed that he was suffering from something of the sort. "The President," he said, "wondered a little about putting you on the committee—he was afraid that being new here you might be intimidated by the trustees. But, basing my views partly on my own impressions and partly on what I have heard from others, particularly Scarlett, I assured him that there was no real danger of that. And he agreed of course. We were all three convinced of your—academic rectitude."

The last two words had been spoken with considered emphasis, and Nick's accumulating sensitivity emphasized them still further. They struck his ears with a sensation almost physically painful.

"Thanks," he said rather hoarsely and then added, "I've got to be getting along—so long, Dr. Pirbright. And—thanks."

He turned abruptly from the path onto the grass and walked a little wildly across it toward Theseion Street. It seemed to him that there was, here in the open air of the campus, as there had been earlier in the Kriedler Memorial Room, and earlier still in the Chapel on the Feast of

the Patron, a Presence, reproachful, admonitory, and alarming, unto whom all hearts were open and from whom he no
longer cared to attempt the hiding of secrets.

The revolution that had begun on the *terrazzo* was zig-
zagging toward completion.

Chapter XIV   Graduation

*A*t nine o'clock the next morning Nick entered Barrowes Hall. His presence there was a substantial victory of reason, intermittently but finally triumphant over fantasy. He had passed a bad night punctuated with the more disturbing varieties of nightmares, and he had emerged from it with a single, urgent notion—the transcendent importance of seeing the President before anything else happened. Armed with a memorized prepared speech, which he proposed to deliver without preface, he passed through the rotunda with glazed eyes averted from Marian's inquiring glance.

As he entered the President's office he wet his lips in readiness for the exacting declamation he had composed during the night. But he had reckoned without the powerful personality of Dr. Overton. It had not occurred to him that the President might have in hand an epic of his own, but this, it immediately became clear, was the case. At Nick's entrance he had been studying some papers on his

295

desk, and without waiting to greet him he held up one of them and read aloud from it in an oratorical roar.

"*Vivet vivetque,*" he cried with formidable emotion, although of a not altogether identifiable sort, "*per omnem seculorum memoriam, dumque hoc vel forte vel providentia utcumque constitutum rerum naturae corpus.*" While speaking he extended one arm in a large rhetorical gesture.

For a man in a high state of nerves who had steeled himself to the business of confessing a crime, this reception was paralyzing. It was odd enough as a form of welcome, but its message contained a relevance still more bizarre. A few of the words Nick recognized, enough to convey an undoubted association with death, and this undid simultaneously his recollection of his own prepared speech and his determination to deliver it.

That determination had been achieved—or, more precisely, accumulated—during the course of the previous night by a process comparable to rolling downhill through a forest, bouncing painfully from tree to tree in an agonizing progress toward the bottom. He had made his decision, knowingly and irrevocably, but he had been badly bruised en route. Both the psychological and the moral imperatives, as Marian had once called them, demanded confession. The afternoon before he had observed, for the first time, the outlines of a moral principle fully revealed. During the night he had concluded that he must conform to it. His knowledge of its existence had corrupted forever his capacity for innocence. Adventure had been transformed into treachery. He had no choice but to plunge into the purifying water whose imagery he had so often and so fluently explained to his students.

And now a Latin quotation robbed him of the formulas with which he had prepared to cleanse himself.

"Has someone died?" he asked.

"Ah, you understand Latin?"

"Some." He did not feel inclined to try to explain the parallels between Latin and Italian.

"Good. I regard Latin as basic, although old-fashioned," said the President heartily. "No, no one has died. In fact Marian told me this morning that he is better." He paused. "Happily," he added, as an afterthought. "But last week, of course, we couldn't be sure. One must be prepared." Resuming a more prosaic manner, he laid down the paper. "It is an excellent eulogy. I shall have it filed. Someone else will die."

"Yes, sir."

"Was it about the meeting yesterday that you wished to see me?" The President unexpectedly winked. "You will be interested to know that I had a long and friendly talk with Dr. Kelly last night. His attitude on life will in the future be, I think, somewhat more"—the President paused —"I shall not say amenable. Nor yet reasonable. Perhaps, more accommodating?" He put this as a question, looking with grave inquiry at Nick, and then immediately amended it. "No, not accommodating. Nor responsible either. More cheerful?"

This surprising adjective was again presented as a query, but Nick failed to make any answer.

"One cannot, of course, foretell the future course of his private life. But I think that he will be more cheerful than in the past. I think we may count on that. And possibly," the President added casually, as if in passing, "more discreet. I might add that Dr. Purview has been exceptionally understanding throughout. But that was not, perhaps, what you wished to see me about after all?"

"No, sir."

"Good. What is it then?"

"What I've come to say is—" Nick stopped. He could not remember what he had come to say. At least he had forgotten the words in which he proposed to say it, and for the moment the result was the same. He swallowed.

"Some matter concerned with your teaching?" the President suggested. He spoke with a sort of outsized gentleness.

Nick found his voice. "Not exactly my teaching, no, sir." He groped for at least some phrase from his prepared speech, but it eluded him. It was clearly necessary to say something. "I am not Stuart Hunter."

"Good," said the President calmly, as if approving a conclusion that he himself had already reached about some minor question of administrative procedure.

"I mean," Nick said idiotically, "really."

"You'd better sit down," the President said.

He remained standing, rigidly. "My name is Nick Torrente."

"Your name is what?" The President appeared to find the name of Nick Torrente more improbable than the fact that it was not Stuart Hunter.

"Nick Torrente. Dominic Torrente. Italian," Nick added by way of making it appear more plausible. "I never got through high school."

"Why not?"

The President's power to surprise him, so often demonstrated in the past, now reduced Nick to a state of reflexive inanity. "I got all As in tenth grade," he said, in a sort of reprise of his remarks to Hunter months before. "I was doing fine. But I needed money. I had to get a job."

"Good," the President said in a tone that was undoubtedly an invitation to further revelations. None was forthcoming, and he added, "What then?"

"I had a lot of jobs. None of them amounted to much. Then I got drafted."

This time it was the President who failed to reply. A soporific calm was settling over his features, and his head sank onto his chest with the familiar, jerky descent. Nick stared at him in dismay. The interview was progressing in a way so unlike what he had anticipated that he could see no point in trying to reconstruct his speech. But a more effective alternative was still eluding him when the President, opening one eye, said, "Go on."

"Well, I got drafted, and they made me an M.P. and sent me to Germany. I used to go down to Italy on leave. I got it fixed up to get my discharge there."

"Why?"

"I liked it. I spoke the language and all, because of my family. And—well, I met Hunter in Rome last summer. He'd changed his mind about coming to teach here, so I said I'd take his place."

"Why?"

"It seemed like a good idea at the time." He was aware that this was inadequate, but it was the only thing that occurred to him.

"Even though you knew nothing whatever about literature? Or education?"

"It was," Nick said hesitantly, "a kind of joke. I boned up on literature."

The President's head was slightly bowed, and he was staring appraisingly from half-closed eyes. He said nothing. Nick was compelled to continue. "I wanted to see if I could do it. I didn't like being called illiterate. I did do it, too," he added with sudden and, he realized, imprudent satisfaction.

"Quite so. Why did you decide to tell me about it, then?"

"I got to worrying. Yesterday, after the meeting."

"Why?"

"I realized that I'd gotten mixed up in something more —serious, I guess, than I'd realized. I saw that everybody here really meant what they were saying. I began to feel that I was being—" He stopped, baffled by the intricacy of what he had begun to feel.

"Blasphemous?" the President suggested, detachedly.

Nick considered. "Maybe."

"What do you propose to do now?"

"I don't know." It was true. His soul-searchings of the night before had taken him no further than this moment.

The President looked at him speculatively. There was, it seemed to Nick, no reason to prolong the interview. The essential facts had been covered. But Dr. Overton's attitude gave no grounds for hoping that he might expect to be immediately dismissed; indeed Nick perceived in his face a peculiar and ominous change of expression, as if an altogether new idea had come to him. The President shook himself slightly, and a faint smile appeared fleetingly on his lips. He appeared to be considering with great care some large and complex project.

It could only be, Nick reflected, a project of a punitive nature. In the protracted pause that ensued he began to contemplate with extreme discomfort and mounting impatience the question of what he did propose to do next. With surprise, he discovered that his attachment to Parthenon was mounting in direct ratio to the impossibility of his remaining in it. But of more immediate concern was a suddenly awakened anxiety about the actual perils of his position. The concern he had felt earlier, that his activities might be criminally actionable, recurred and was at once supplemented by a still more lively anxiety as to whether they might not be certifiable. The President's attitude suggested very tolerably that of an administrator dealing with a lunatic who required careful handling.

Or perhaps, he concluded after considering the course of the interview so far, a recalcitrant schoolboy. The President's calculating eye seemed to him, the longer he looked at it, embarrassing rather than alarming, as if he were deliberately engaged in transforming the scale of Nick's misdeeds from the monumental to the fractious. The threat of imprisonment or certification waned and was replaced by the prospect of being spanked.

Nick was suddenly angry. Confession had availed nothing, it seemed, but humiliation. Catharsis, so warmly advocated by students of English 49 as psychic therapy, was conferring none of its benefits upon him. The silence continued, and Nick's jaw went out.

"Good." The President resumed the conversation in a startling crescendo. "And so, you never finished high school?"

"No."

"You worked at odd jobs. You were drafted. You were sent to Germany. You were discharged in Italy. What were you doing after you were discharged? I take it you remained in Italy?"

"Yes, I did."

"For how long?"

"Three years."

"What were you doing?"

"I was a sort of private secretary."

"To whom?"

To this inquisition, as unnecessary in Nick's view as it was belittling, he responded with extreme irritation. Whatever the proprieties of his position in Lady Tarragon's household, it was, he conceived, no business of President Overton's. But he had no impulse to conceal it.

"To an English viscountess," he said. "Very wealthy."

The President looked at him with a steady stare. "You were her *private* secretary?" he asked meaningly.

"That's right."

"Ah," said the President.

Nick's impatience mounted. He could see no reason for a further exploration of his past. The essential facts had been adequately covered. There was nothing more that had to be said.

"What has become of Hunter?"

Nick started. He had, he was obliged to admit, been wrong in supposing that the supply of relevant information was exhausted. This was an entirely pertinent question.

"He's all right. He was here last week."

"I know he was. Why did he come?"

"He changed his mind about staying in Italy. He—" Nick hesitated. "He felt he ought to tell you what had happened."

"But he didn't?"

"No, sir. He changed his mind again."

"An unstable young man." The President seemed to be on the verge of another smile. "Why?"

"I—talked him out of it."

"How?"

"I—told him it wouldn't do him any good to make a scene, since it was as much his fault as mine. At least," Nick continued, realizing that so misleading a summary of his transactions with Hunter must be amended, "I tricked him into thinking that."

"He is not actually deranged, as you explained in advance?"

"No, sir. He was pretty upset, but he wasn't crazy."

"Where is he now?"

"He went back to Italy. I gave him some money. He's going to work on his book. In Florence."

"Is he content to do that?"

"I—I don't know."

"What was he doing before he came here?"

"He stayed in Italy."

"What was he doing there?"

"He was resting."

"*Resting?*"

"Well, yes, for a while."

"He hasn't been resting since last summer?"

"No, sir."

Whatever the nature of his suspicions, the President's curiosity about the activities of Stuart Hunter was clearly aroused. He was, it was regrettably apparent, determined to probe further. "What *was* he doing?"

"Well, he took over my old job."

"As—private secretary to this viscountess?" The President's massive calm was disturbed. He was clearly surprised. "And what is her name?"

Nick told him.

And in the next half hour he told him a great deal more besides. The President was left in no doubt about the nature of Lady Tarragon's arrangements. The remarkable events that had transacted themselves on the *terrazzo* were unfolded. Details of Nick's early years were revealed. The methods by which Nick had mastered the subject of American literature and the arts of teaching were explored. The situation was, in short, laid fully open by the President's skilled action with the inquisitorial knife.

"Good," he said when the state of affairs had been fully investigated. "I think that is all I need to know."

Nick was glad to hear it. He was exhausted.

And then Dr. Overton did a still more surprising thing. He laughed. His laughter was loud and violent. He was almost literally doubled up with it. After some minutes of this orgy he was gasping painfully for breath, but still he laughed. The heights of the room echoed to his laughter.

"Good," he said at length, panting. "Very good." He wiped tears from his eyes. "I have been hoping for years for a really good joke to be played on this faculty. I never, however, expected one half so good as this. You," he pointed a finger still shaking slightly, "are a young man of really extraordinary wit and resource. You show us all how vulnerable we are. I congratulate you. You have done a bold and salutary deed.

"Speaking as priest as well as president," Dr. Overton continued, "I must say that the thing that strikes me most is not that you succeeded in evading detection but that you gave yourself up of your own choice as a result of a moral decision after you had parried all the threats of exposure."

"They parried themselves," Nick said. "Some of them anyway. I feel guilty as hell, Dr. Overton."

"An apposite comparison. What do you feel guilty of?"

"Well, for one thing, I feel guilty about Dean Scarlett. I think he'd found out something. Maybe it brought on his stroke."

"I am absolutely confident, Mr. Torrente, that your problem had nothing to do with it. I have already spoken to the doctors. He was much sicker than he knew. It might have happened at any time. You may be assured that you have nothing at all to blame yourself for. Scarlett is a man with a sense of humor—the only one around here except for ourselves, I sometimes think. He would appreciate this as much as I. Erase from your mind any feeling of responsibility, Mr. Torrente. You are guiltless."

This statement produced in Nick a surge of relief. "But even if I haven't anything to blame myself for about Dean Scarlett, I'm guilty of a good many other things." He paused, searching for a word to summarize his guilt. "Blasphemy," he concluded.

"Speaking," the President said, "as a priest, I may assure you that you are wrong. Speaking as a college president, I am obliged to agree with you. You are guilty of serious misconduct." He paused. "Serious, and inconvenient. But not, I think, unforgivable. You have, I take it, not knowingly lied to the students—about anything, that is, except your name and qualifications?"

Nick considered. This question opened up new channels of thought. "No, not knowingly."

"You have not sought to deride in any way the value of learning, or scholarship, or of the life of the mind?"

"No, sir, I certainly haven't."

"In that case—" The President stopped as if the matter had been disposed of, and paused. "You will no doubt be interested to know of a letter I have recently received. From Dr. Campion in Oregon."

Nick gasped.

"Dr. Campion met Scarlett in Los Angeles before he was taken ill. In his letter he described a conversation they had. He did not at first hear of Scarlett's collapse and as soon as he realized that Scarlett had not been able to report to me he wrote. He seems to have concluded that you were involved in the Mafia, or the narcotics trade, or very likely both." The President paused and looked at him sternly. "Are you?"

"No, sir."

"No, I didn't suppose so. You understand that we can't possibly let you go on teaching here? That *would* be unforgivable, not on your part but on mine. Nor may you continue to call yourself a doctor of philosophy. That will raise problems."

"Problems? What problems?"

"Practical problems. Serious, but not, I imagine, insoluble. On the other hand it is not illegal in New York State to call yourself by an assumed name, as I understand it. I am glad to say that anybody can call himself anything he likes, provided of course it is not for criminal purposes. I rejoice in the fact. It is one of the few liberties that a provident government has left us."

Nick had no reply to this digression.

"You would, I take it, not object to being called Hunter permanently? The name is not obnoxious to you?"

"I don't see . . ."

"It might be possible," the President said, "to change your name legally, by court order. Quietly, after a year or two. It would no doubt simplify your affairs."

"My affairs?"

"During the course of our little chat," the President said blandly, "I have been considering the question—a very vexing question, for the matter is urgent—of a successor to Dean Scarlett. Quite frankly, Mr. Torrente, you strike me as the right man for the post. You are familiar with the college. You are resourceful. You are, I think, just what this faculty has needed in the way of new ideas for a very long time. A fresh outlook, if you understand me? We shall have the youngest Dean of Students in the country. That ought to please the foundations."

Nick looked at him blankly.

"And I know that Scarlett will be delighted to have you as his successor, especially when the nature of your—masquerade has been explained to him. The practical difficulties may be got around with a little thought. We might for example arrange a leave of absence after a year or two to enable you to complete your high-school education. We might even be able to arrange for an honorary degree from some other institution. I am, of course, acquainted with various channels in such matters. And there is no need whatever for anyone here to know anything about your—ah—background, except ourselves. It would be much better to keep your background confidential."

"Yes, sir," Nick said faintly.

"There may possibly be some problem about Hunter. If he stays in Italy, all is well. If not, I might be able to find him a position in some other college. I don't myself much fancy the sound of him, but it would help to straighten things out for him. I also know channels for making such an arrangement should it become desirable."

"Yes, sir."

"I have already composed a letter to Dr. Campion explaining matters. I shall tell him that the whole thing was a complicated wager, as I take it from your account it was; that Stuart Hunter is in Italy completing his book and is no way to blame for what happened; and that you have been removed from your teaching duties. I take it that you will be able to deal with Lady Tarragon should she ever present any problem?"

"Yes, sir."

"Your students get on well with you?"

"Yes, sir."

"I am sure so, judging from the *Achaean* poll and other reports."

"Yes, sir."

"And you were once a military policeman?"

"Yes, sir."

"That will provide you with admirable training for dealing with undergraduates. Better than Scarlett's, I imagine. And you were this woman's paramour?"

"Yes, sir."

"That will give you most useful understanding of student psychology." He paused. "Will you accept the appointment? Subject to the trustees' approval, although that is only a formality?"

"Yes, sir."

"Good." President Overton rose to shake hands. "I congratulate you. And I congratulate myself."

"Yes, sir," Nick said.

He walked out into the rotunda in a condition that resembled with singular exactness one of advanced intoxication. His reaction to the President's offer combined dizziness, elation, and confusion. Distances seemed at the moment very large indeed, but his capacity to cover them was correspondingly increased.

He saw Marian. Stopping in front of her desk, he felt a curious surge of triumph. Obstacles, he perceived, were evanescing all around him. A peculiar symmetry was replacing the labyrinthine intricacies of his relations with her. It was going to be hard to explain, but, he suddenly realized, not impossible. He was still an impostor—an eximpostor, anyway. He was still tied to Acropolis, and to the academic world. But these two things were no longer a double obstacle—by the fissionable effect of the last hour's nuclear reaction they had suddenly cancelled themselves out. He could now present himself in his own identity. He could reveal himself as appropriately debauched.

He looked at her speculatively across the desk, and she saw in his face so odd an expression, at once bold and enigmatic, that she rose from her chair. Something strange had certainly happened to him, but she was as unprepared for the words that he spoke as she had been for the manic glint in his eyes.

"I don't believe we've met," he said. "My name is Dominic Torrente."

She stared, considering what could possibly have happened in his long conversation with the President to unseat his reason.

"My name is Dominic Torrente, and I never finished high school, but the President has just appointed me Dean of Students. And . . ."

She was still staring, but the presumption of his madness had left her mind. She had begun to smile, and Nick saw in her eyes more than simply astonishment.